THE EASTER RISING

From Easter week, 1916, and its glories,
through the aftermath of civil war, the
unsettled 'thirties, and the shooting of
innocents such as Constable Anderson,
'The Red-Gold Flame' is an exciting
documentary on a period of Irish history
that has all the elements of a
high-tension thriller. It is a book that
will appeal to all Englishmen who wish
to understand the Irish, all Irishmen who
want to shed inhibitions about the English,
and those two lots of Irish who are just
beginning to talk to each other again
across the border. . . .

A. V. SELLWOOD

THE RED-GOLD FLAME

CORGI BOOKS
A DIVISION OF TRANSWORLD PUBLISHERS

THE RED-GOLD FLAME

A CORGI BOOK

First publication in Great Britain

PRINTING HISTORY
Corgi Edition published 1966

This book is set in
9/9½pt. Times

Corgi Books are published by Transworld Publishers Ltd.,
Bashley Road, London, N.W.10
Made and printed in Great Britain by
Hunt Barnard & Co., Ltd., Aylesbury, Bucks.

"Who fears to speak of Easter week,
Who dares its fate deplore?
The red-gold flame of Erin's name
Confronts the world once more . . ."

Rebel song to the tune of
" The Men of '98"

The back cover photographs are reproduced by kind permission of Radio Times Hulton Picture Library.

"Irishmen and Irishwomen. In the Name
of God and of the dead generations
from which she received her old traditions
of nationhood, Ireland, through us,
summons her children to her flag and
strikes for her freedom . . ."

Start of the proclamation
of the republican 'Provisional
Government', Easter Monday, 1916

"Whereas an attempt instigated and designed by
the foreign enemies of our King and Country
to incite rebellion in Ireland and thus endanger
the safety of the United Kingdom has been made
by a reckless though small body of men who have
been guilty of insurrectionary action in the
City of Dublin . . ."

Start of the proclamation issued
by Lord Wimborne, the British Viceroy

CHAPTER ONE

It was a brilliantly sunlit morning, the start of a week of splendid weather: June in April they said. Between the grey stone piers of Kingstown Harbour, six miles to the south of the city, small boats bobbed at their moorings and nudged each other on the slightest of sea swells. On the lettuce-green slopes of the Dublin mountains the holiday-making crowds —arriving there by jaunting car, pony and trap and tram, were beginning to spread themselves and their picnic baskets; ready to enjoy with their children what promised to be the hottest Spring day in living memory. In Phoenix Park, over to the city's west, the one hundred and more windows of the Vice-regal Lodge, residence of His Excellency Lord Wimborne, stared blankly over razored lawns, and dark cypress trees unswayed by any wind. Above the four-columned portico that formed the centre of this stately palace the tall flagstaff gleamed in new paint. The red, white and blue flag clung to it like a lover. To Captain Robert Knight, sauntering towards the O'Connell Bridge across the Liffey, Dublin looked even lovelier than he'd been told: the "jewel" of a city, they'd described it, when urging him to go there on convalescent leave. "A week of peace," his pet V.A.D. had said "will soon drive away those noises in your head . . ."

Even in the hospital in Kent, Knight had been haunted by the echoes of that conflict in Flanders mud that had thrown him, at 29, on the casualty scrap-heap; to be salvaged for later use. Each day he could hear the guns—whatever the others might say—like the distant slamming shut of giant doors. Nightmares had haunted him long after his wound was healed. Yet now, for the first time, he felt rested and relaxed.

The three brother officers who had accompanied Knight to Ireland had left the Home early, to be drawn, with most of the city garrison it would seem, towards the epicentre of the day's masculine social routine: the races at Fairyhouse. But Knight had preferred to mooch around on his own, discover for himself, and savour the charm of, this most elegant and hospitable of cities. After walking up the coast road, delighted by the music of the sea, he had crossed the canal that lay to the city's south by way of Mount Street

Bridge. And there he had loitered for a little while, in the quiet tree-lined Georgian squares and crescents on the route to Grafton Street, the Bond Street of fashionable Dublin. Now O'Connell Bridge lay before him, and behind him the Castle clock struck melodiously the hour. Eleven o'clock.

* * *

Down near the wharfside on North Wall, in a smoke-grimed building of peeling paint and uncompromising ugliness, a stout, moustachioed, and slightly bandy figure was strapping a Sam Brown over a vivid green uniform jacket and scandalising some of those in his immediate vicinity by singing, on this day of resurrection:

"For we've another Saviour now,
That Saviour is the Sword . . ."

Around this red-cheeked, ebullient and superbly confident fellow, there was noise and bustle and movement, and shouted words of command. There was also, from the dark depths of the building, the clang of steel on steel: the hammering of the armourer. For this was not only the stronghold of militant Labour in Dublin: it was the H.Q. and arsenal of a private army, the Citizen's Army. In short, the famous, or notorious, Liberty Hall.

As befitted the place that authority described as " the centre of social anarchy in Ireland, the brain of every riot and disturbance," the flag that flaunted itself before the faithful now gathered there was of different colour to that which hung above the Vice-regal Lodge. A green flag, worked with the emblem of the Plough and the Stars. Red could be worn in Liberty Hall, they used to wisecrack, but never in conjunction with white and blue.

"For we've another Saviour now,
That Saviour is the Sword . . ."

"What the hell does he have to sing *that* for?" asked a worried volunteer, as, his boots clattering on the shabby lino of the stairs, he hastened to the parade that was now forming up in the unheroic surroundings of proletarian Beresford Place.

His companion shrugged, and grinned. "Don't begrudge the Boss his bit of a song. I like to hear it—it means he's feeling grand."

At 48, James Connolly would probably have agreed with this description of the state of his morale. There had been times in recent weeks when even the Connolly over-allotment of sturdy optimism and indefatigable fighting zeal had seemed in need of replenishment, affected by the uncertainties of others, less self-sure. But now he was in top form: felt a veritable giant among men. The die was cast. There could be no turning back. The thing he had wanted to do—had devoted half of his life in planning to do—was soon to be a fact: whatever its outcome might be. Reserve abandoned him.

As, flanked by his aides, he went downstairs to inspect the parade, he paused briefly to shake hands with a close friend waiting in the dark and odiferous hall.

"What chance do you think we've got, Jim?" the other asked.

James Connolly paused, and then, as if considering the question for the very first time, and as if it related to something of as remote concern to his future as life on a distant planet, answered decisively: "Not a dog's chance. No chance at all. They'll slaughter the lot of us!"

"Then why the . . .?"

But already the Commandant General of the Citizen Army, and, for this occasion, the commander of operations in the field for its new-found ally, the Irish Volunteers, had resumed his genial grin and stepped into the sunshine. At a snapped command his army, brought itself to attention.

Connolly beamed upon them—all four hundred of them. He was proud of them. They would not let him down. Together he and that dreamer Padraic Pearse, who had seized control of the Irish Volunteers, were about to implement the ambition that had for so long dominated their separate, and otherwise so dissimilar, patterns of thought. In an hour from now the "army" would be at war. At War with England.

*   *   *

It was nearly noon. As Knight strolled over the O'Connell Bridge—the flower bed down its centre bursting with daffodils —his strangely enchanted mood persisted. Ahead of him, beyond the grandiose monument to the Great Emancipator who gave the bridge its name, the crowds in their Sunday best thronged the pavements of the straight street that stretched towards the north. At the top end, Nelson's Pillar, slightly masking the Parnell Monument, looked down in lonely magnificence on four rows of glittering track, where bobbed and swayed like ships the trams of Dublin Corporation, packed with holidaymakers. On each side stretched as far as the eye could see a vista of elegant stores,

11

exclusive restaurants, the theatres that had made the city the new "rage" of the intellectuals. Deliciously, Knight pondered on just where he would lunch. Continue up the street towards the Gresham? Or turn back for Stephen's Green, and the equally pleasing opulence of the Shelbourne? He was still enjoying being undetermined about it, when he was aware of something disturbing happening in front of him. And quite abruptly, all his feeling of wellbeing disappeared. Once more he felt the touch—the warning touch—of Flanders send reflex actions to his brain and muscle. He was alert for tragedy.

At first Knight could not trace the reason for his unease. "I've been overdoing things," he thought, in a effort to rationalise. "It's imagination, just as they said in the hospital." And then—almost to his relief—he identified it. The pattern of the crowd in the street: it was changing before his eyes. Most people were still sauntering casually past the gleaming shop windows: but some had quickened their pace. And some had streamed off the kerb, and into the road, and were beginning to run—towards the north.

"What's up?" he called to a jarvie. "What are they running for?"

The man looked down from the box above the flyblown nag that had jogged with the hansom from the streets leading to the East. "It's the volunteers, sir," he said. "But you wouldn't want to be worrying about the likes of them . . ."

"The volunteers?"

"Yes sir, the bloody Sinn Feiners," the jarvie spat. "The cheek of them now—playing at soldiers and marching through the streets. They ought to be ashamed of themselves, on such a holiday as this."

Knight was just about to book the cab to take him to the Shelbourne when he thought that—for the devil of it—he'd have a look at these extraordinary chaps who, until now, he had only heard about third-hand.

"Well, it's each man to his taste," said the jarvie without malice. "And there's one thing sure, sir—you'll be able to have a good laugh . . ."

* * *

"Statue of Justice, mark well her station
Her face to the Castle, her back to the nation . . ."

The ironic doggerel, so much beloved by Dubliners of all degree, and every shade of political thought, was probably far from the mind of Major Ivor Price of military intelligence as he hurried through the great gateway and passed under the twin leaden statues of Justice and Fortitude that graced the clocktower from which Knight had heard the hour strike just forty minutes before.

Three days had passed since a Sinn Fein plot had been uncovered: a plot for a nation-wide uprising, aided by Germany. It had come to light with the capture of that "traitor" Sir Roger Casement, when landed by submarine near Tralee Bay. Almost simultaneously, a German ship had been detained, loaded with 20,000 rifles to arm the disaffected in the provinces. Yet, after a series of confidences, Authority had done nothing. Apart from Casement and his associates in the west, not one would-be rebel had been detained or questioned, despite angry calls for action by the Viceroy himself.

It was true, of course, that the German ship and her cargo now rested at the bottom of Queenstown Harbour. True also that the malcontents appeared to have had second thoughts. A dramatic advertisement had appeared in the Irish Independent, calling off the "manoeuvres" that the Irish Volunteers were to have carried out on Sunday: the "manoeuvres" that, it was now obvious, were to have sparked off revolt. Price had—at first—doubts about the genuineness of this Countermanding Order, signed by the Volunteers' President, Eoin MacNeill. But, when Sunday dawned, such doubts were eased, and, as the day progressed with no excitement, it had been decided that a mortal blow had been struck to those who harboured insurrectionary sentiments: more, it now transpired that there had been a split within the Volunteer organisation —that O'Neill, unlike his lieutenant Padraic Pearse, was opposed to the idea of an uprising at this stage, and had been shocked to hear of plans being made "behind his back." All the same, Price had been inclined to support Lord Wimborne's view: that Ireland could not rest safe until the Volunteer leadership was under lock and key. He was relieved to feel that—to judge by the urgency of this holiday morning summons to the Castle—Sir Matthew Nathan, Under Secretary for Ireland, had been converted to the Viceroy's point of view.

Close on Price's heels came another visitor to the stony symbol of the imperial rule in Ireland. Mr Norway, secretary to the Post Office. Unlike the Captain, this high civil servant was puzzled by the nature of Nathan's call, but gathered it had something to do with the cypher telegram that, only the day before, had been sent to London, with a top priority rating on it, for Mr Birrell, Nathan's immediate superior. Not much was seen in Ireland of Augustine Birrell these days. He was seldom in the land where, ostensibly, he governed.

As Norway passed through the gate, the sentry on duty there smartly presented arms, then relapsed to the stand-easy and, doubtless, a state of boredom.

All but thirty-five of the Castle garrison—usually a company strong—had been sent on leave. The sentry was one of the unlucky few.

* * *

It was in 1205 when Henry II—of unhappy memory to the Celts—directed Meiller FitzHenry to build the first Dublin Castle. He was given permission to build the place where he chose: but there was one very significant proviso. It must be "to *curb* the city as to defend it, if occasion shall require."

"Occasion," since then, had quite often "so required."

On this morning of sunshine and gay holiday, however, there was little thought of the Castle's gloomy past among the crowds who promenaded outside its open gates. Nor was there in its untidy profusion of architectural styles, much hint of the lowering edifice of grey stone that had been so grimly cemented with the blood of Norman and Celt. FitzHenry's fortress had occupied no more than what was now known as the Upper Castle Yard. In seven centuries the place had been rebuilt and so much extended, that it was almost a town in itself. A maze of state apartments, government offices, quarters for top-level civil servants, and, for its garrison, an annex—Ship Street Barracks. It housed a chapel, a former Mint, and stately Georgian ballrooms. In its hospital there rested over seventy wounded soldiers, home from the Front.

It was to an unpretentious and rather gloomy office not very far from the guardroom that the trim-moustached and swarthy Sir Matthew Nathan—he had formerly been Governor of Hongkong—now went to keep his tryst with his two subordinates. To him, the occasion was one for sombre introspection. Loyal to his chief—Augustine Birrell—he had shared much of the other's belief in leaving the exponents of the new Irish nationalism a greater degree of liberty than that usually tolerated by what was known as "Castle Government". He even recognised—or appears to have recognised—that, after the failure to act against Carson's Ulster Volunteers, banded in arms to resist Westminster's Home Rule pledge, action aimed solely at disarming the secessionist private armies would be equivocal, to say the least. All the

14

same he must now have had doubts over certain aspects of his adherence to laissez-faire.

When, on December 15, Lord Middleton—"as mouthpiece of an influential body of Irishmen"—had brought intimation of the hatching of insurrectionary ambitions, Birrell had said "I laugh at the whole thing!" But only after Nathan had described the allegations as "vague." When Major General Friend, the G.O.C. Ireland, had wished to react sharply after Volunteers had fired on an angry crowd in the west, it was the Birrell-Nathan team that had once more stamped upon "oppressive" policies. Price himself had encountered the force of their displeasure.

Only two or three weeks before the events that now had forced the Assistant Secretary to call him to conference, the intelligence officer had intercepted a letter from a prominent Sinn Feiner to supporters in America, anticipating that a rising was near. "Vague" had once more been Sir Matthew Nathan's comment. To which his chief had added, in the margin "Rubbish!"

Right to the last, Nathan had maintained his stand against the "hotheads" of the police and army, demanding action. As recently as yesterday, he had met Lord Wimborne's plan to arrest sixty to a hundred of the Sinn Fein leaders by vigorous stone-walling, referring the matter back to London. Arrest and suppression would only lead to bloodshed. And bloodshed was what Birrell and he had bent backwards to avoid. Until today. . . .

*   *   *

A straggling line of men and boys, some of them wearing the green uniforms of the Citizen Army, others the heather-green of the Irish Volunteers, but most of them, the vast majority, in workaday clothes that were supplemented only by bandoliers and armbands came marching, or rather shuffling, around the corner of Abbey Street, from the east, and then wheeled right towards Upper O'Connell Street.

"Good for a laugh!" Knight recalled—that jarvie had not exaggerated.

He was astonished at the unsoldierlike appearance of those men, whose open ambition was one day to put paid to British rule. They couldn't put paid to the regimental cat! And yet, on reflection, he had to admit that the Brigade of Guards itself might not have shaped very well—not if lumbered, as these fellows were, with such odd lines of equipment.

Probably nine out of every ten of the volunteers carried

15

rifles, but they were rifles of practically every shape and size. Occasionally he could see service type Lee-Enfields—indignantly he wondered where they'd come from—but the rest were a hotch-potch, procured from all over the world. Martini carbines, the odd Winchester, the American Springfield, and — predominating in numbers — the single shot German Mauser: even in the Boer War considered obsolescent. However, it was on the rest of the gear that so oppressed the column that Knight's fascinated eyes lingered the longest. All of the men were top-heavy with equipment, but it was equipment of a type that no other military force had ever taken on parade. Suitcases . . . corn bags . . . even brown paper parcels tied with string . . . these unsoldierlike items the marchers somehow carried along with them, together with an extraordinary array of tools. They carried spades, pickaxes, crowbars and hatchets and spare weapons that included shotguns and swords. A few even stepped it out beneath antique spears and pikes.

"How jolly extraordinary!" thought Knight.

To complete the atmosphere of slaphappy improvisation that—deceptively it was to transpire—appeared to dominate the column, a hansom and a jaunting car brought up the rear, providing what was evidently the "army's" transport. Both were piled high with ammunition boxes, secured by straps and ropes, and flanked by a score or so women; now and then stepping out to embrace their embarrassed menfolk, or help carry part of the equipment's overspill. Ahead of the marchers stepped four officers in uniform, their heads crowned with Boer-type slouch hats.

"You *bloody* traitors!" screamed a man in the crowd.

Jerked back from his reverie of half-pitying contempt, Knight found his mood hardening. Bloody traitors, yes that was the phrase all right. Irishmen were dying in France, dying in tens of thousands, while these fellows talked of their coming war against England. And no one lifted a single finger to stop them. It wasn't right!

It was with an effort that, at that moment, he restrained his temper. But restraint was definitely the order of the day. The volunteers were always carrying out their war games—he'd been warned about them, before his leave began. And the answer was to ignore them; and not get involved in incidents. Leave them alone, it was said, and their publicity stunts would merely make them ridiculous. Such was the theory held by remote Whitehall. At the moment it seemed reasonable enough.

But then, as he glanced once more at the silent men—not answering the abuse directed at them but patiently trudging on—the Captain was caught by something that was totally out of character with the thinking that had governed his briefing. And out of character too, with the jarvie's "good for a laugh."

He saw it in the eyes of those who formed this burlesque of a parade—a dedicated passion, a strange and unearthly beauty, a sublimation of feeling that moved his mind to remembrance. So had shone the eyes of his friends as, for the first time, they had taken the road to battle: knowing nothing of the disillusionment to come, prepared only for sacrifice.

*   *   *

"Them two together, Padraic Pearse and Connolly!" disgustedly exclaimed a woman at Knight's side. "Did you ever see the like? Oil and water will mix better than the Volunteers and Connolly's bunch of reds."

"If they ever use their popguns, it'll be against each other . . ." said her companion, amiably agreeing.

Knight, listening to them, failed to understand.

Fact was however that few of those in the know regarding the personalities and general political outlook of the men who now led the column towards the north end of O'Connell Street—and its fateful destiny—would have expected a year or so back to have seen them on friendly terms, let alone in a partnership where each relied to the death on the other's loyalty. The down-to-earth and roughtongued Connolly, the tall and darkly handsome Padraic Pearse: each came from a different end of the social scale, and in all things but their antipathy towards an alien rule, had philosophies that were literally worlds apart.

On the one hand, marched the rugged organiser of the Irish Transport and General Workers Union, who had founded the Citizen's Army purely as a worker's weapon in a war of strikes and lockouts, fought at the factory gates. On the other, the introspective intellectual and poet, absorbed in gaelic lore, gaelic teaching, gaelic speaking and with a social background far removed from the black industrial jungle in which Connolly had so toughly struggled to the top. Strange bedfellows these, to be allies in revolution.

Self-taught the hard way, studying after long hours of backbreaking physical labour, James Connolly was probably in his day the West's most convinced believer in the Marxist theory of direct action: while the gently-bred Pearse—

intensely religious, and drawing from the legends of saints and heroes of the past the inspiration, and absolution, for his attempts to mould the present—was the epitome of the Nationalist idealist, the exponent of Ireland as a Nation, with followers whose every interest might be expected to impel them to make short shrift of socialism.

Considering these differences, there were many who would have echoed the words overheard by Knight. In the fight against the British the two men might make a formidable coalition. In the rare event of success against the British, each partner might well be a danger to the other. "Hold on to your arms once the day is won," James Connolly was reported to have told his Citizen Army. "You never know when we might need them again."

And yet, whatever their wide and sincerely-held divergencies in politics, each of these men was, for the time being at least, dependent on the other. And each had brought to the one great cause they held in common his own particular brand of talent, as well as courage. To Pearse was to fall the lot of providing the intellectual raison d'etre, the moral justification, the spirit that created the very life of revolt, while to Connolly, worldly-wise, fell the task of shaping and moulding the raw material into which that spirit had been breathed—of coaxing men, cajoling them, and even conning them—driving them on to prodigious exertions when strength of body failed.

"There are worse things than the shedding of blood," the brooding Pearse philosophised. "And one of them is slavery . . ."

Sonorously, James Connolly had declaimed, "Without the slightest trace of irreverence, but in all due humility and awe, we recognise that for us, as of mankind before Calvary, it maye be truly said, 'Without the shedding of Blood there is no redemption'."

Whatever else might divide the socialist and the nationalist it certainly was not lack of enthusiasm for battle, or confidence in the rightness of their current mutual cause.

* * *

It was a truly astonishing spectacle—this parade of men in arms, pledged to overthrow the regime whose police and troops looked on. Nor was it confined to O'Connell Street alone. All over Dublin the volunteers were on the move.

South of the Liffey, to the east, they were marching into Boland's flour mills and Westland Row station, to mask Beggar's Bush barracks, and occupying bridges on the canal that bisected the route from Kingstown Harbour. In this section, their Commandant was a gangling teacher of Gaelic, Eamonn de Valera. One of "Dev's" first moves was to dismantle the city's Gasworks, to lessen the danger of fire and explosion in the mains during the shelling that he—unlike Connolly—saw as an inevitable accompaniment of a British counter-attack.

To the far southwest John Kent was deploying his men among the labyrinth of workhouses, hospitals and nurses' homes that constituted the South Dublin Union, and then installing outposts in the distilleries behind them—to mask Richmond Barracks and the approach from Islandbridge.

To the South-centre, where St Stephens Green and its park marked the hub of nine major roads, marched a Citizen Army contingent under Commandant Mallin; accompanied by the women and Fianna (Republican Scout) detachments commanded by the flamboyant Countess Markievicz.

South of the park-like spot where this wayward scion of the Anglo-Irish ascendancy—the wife of a Polish Count—preached social revolution, two poets were preparing to play a martial part, in the unlikely environment of Jacob's Biscuit Factory. One of the pair was the I.R.B.'s Thomas McDonagh, by rank a Commandant. The other was Patrick Kearney, a humble volunteer. Unlike Donagh, Pearse, and the eccentric, and very sick, Joseph Mary Plunkett, son of a papal Count, Kearney's verse was not well known in "intellectual" circles. A gentle patriot, however, he had written the words for a song that the Rising and its trials was to introduce to history. The Soldier's Song was to become the Irish National Anthem.

North of the river Liffey, and to the immediate westward flank of the headquarters group that had occupied the Post Office, Commandant Ned Daly had marched his Volunteers into the Four Courts, the Irish equivalent of the Law Courts, and captured its one-man "garrison", an unarmed P.C. Now they were throwing up barricades in the neighbouring streets.

It was happening—the Rebellion—in half a dozen places at once. And the bitter joke was that so few appeared to know it.

*   *   *

Irritatedly the police brought traffic to a halt—as the column led by Pearse and Connolly—the headquarters group of the insurgent army—marched towards their rendezvous. These fellows were a bloody nuisance with their provocative manoeuvres. Not a month went by without their doing their stuff. Time that Authority—as the police chiefs had demanded —allowed one to put one's heavy boot down on them.

From among the people whom the marchers claimed to champion, came few cheers, more boos and a monumental indifference. Most Dubliners had relatives at the front, and had little use for those who—quite unfairly—had been represented as being on the Kaiser's payroll. But they'd seen such parades before and they could not even summon up anger. It was all such a waste of time.

The marchers came to a halt just below Nelson's Pillar, where the massive grey stone structure of the Post Office spread itself along the right hand of the street, dominating the blocks around it.

Connolly stepped forward, and drew his sword. "Soldiers of Ireland, right turn!"

A sudden silence fell. Knight, who, despite himself, had somehow felt impelled to follow this strange procession, once more felt that touch of warning on his brain.

"Soldiers of Ireland," yelled Connolly, "CHARGE!"

In a moment the crowd had scattered in confusion, as the volunteers, their paraphernalia left behind them, had charged headlong at the Post Office, disappearing into its depths.

"How very extraordinary," thought Knight.

* * *

In his office in Dublin Castle, isolated by the river from the echoes of the strange goings-on in O'Connell Street, Nathan received his guests and went unwontedly straight to the points. The Viceroy's demand to London had been met. The leaders of the Sinn Fein movement, the Volunteers, and Connolly's Citizen's Army were to be arrested and held. The operation would be conducted in two or three days' time: to save bloodshed, at an hour when the men could be seized in their beds.

It was, for Nathan, a bitter announcement to have to make. And the result of a decision that must have been even more painful for Birrell, whose signature had been required to make the order valid. But now there was nothing for it, but to go speedily ahead: and do the job as expeditiously as they could.

But scarcely had the three men—even now the Attorney General appears to have been excluded from discussion— begun to deliberate on Nathan's words, when there came from the direction of the Gate a volley of shots, followed by a cheer.

20

Price, fumbling for his revolver, dashed to the door and out into Castle Yard. He opened hurried fire at a dozen shapes disappearing into the guardroom, and then ran into two members of the Castle staff. They were carrying the body of a policeman.

"It's P.C. O'Brien," one of them explained in breathless haste. "They shot him when he tried to stop them rushing the gate."

"The Volunteers are up, and have seized the guardroom," said the other.

"The devil!" exploded Price, then remembered with fury that the guard had been issued with blank cartridges only: to avoid "incidents".

He went back to Nathan's office, and grabbed the telephone. But no one answered.

The lines had been cut.

CHAPTER TWO

It was only a few minutes after the volunteers had disappeared into the Post Office that the completely mystified crowd—it now seemed that all Dublin was converging on the spot—were treated to yet another slice of drama: the mass exodus, in sheer panic, of clerks, telephonists and customers, and almost simultaneously, the emergence of two uniformed figures on the ornamental ledge above the portico. As the men worked cautiously past the ledge's centre—point where the Royal Coat of Arms hung dizzily over the street, the crowd fell silent, and then there came from it a long collective sigh; the voice of a distant sea.

The men had attached two small blobs to the halliards of the twin post office flagstaffs. And now the blobs resolved themselves into flags. One of them was the old green flag of Ireland, with harp in centre and—a device of Connolly's—a phrase embroidered all along its length; Irish Republic. The other was at this stage unfamiliar, but soon to be better known. The tricolour: the Orange, Green and White . . .

From the Post Office echoed startlingly a volley of musketry: a fête de joie.

The tall figure of Padraic Pearse reappeared, and came to attention in front of the central doorway, Connolly and other leaders ranged behind him. In his hand, Pearse held a roll of parchment. From this, he now proceeded to read: in the name of "the Provisional Government."

*   *   *

"Irishmen and Irishwomen. In the name of God and the dead generations from which she received her old tradition of nationhood, Ireland, through us, summons her children to her flag and strikes for her freedom. . . ." The Proclamation, delivered in Pearse's remarkably fine voice, had an odd effect on the crowd. It listened in a profound silence.

"In every generation the Irish people have asserted their right to national freedom and sovereignty. Six times during the past three hundred years they have asserted it in arms. . . ." The silence was as unstirring as the ranks of the green uniformed men, who, rifles in hand, were now asserting their place in the history of the island.

"We declare the right of the people of Ireland to the

ownership of Ireland and to the unfettered control of Irish destinies, to be sovereign and indefeasible. . . ." The charm was broken within seconds of the ending of Pearse's delivery. After a feeble cheer, jeers and catcalls came from every side.

The astonished Knight saw the downstairs windows of the Post Office suddenly splinter and dissolve. Then came a persistent hammering crunch: pickaxes at work. So *that* was why these fellows had lumbered themselves with iron-mongery! "They're smashing loopholes in the walls," he said aloud.

A woman in the crowd cried out to him, "God bless your honour—you'll send these bowsies running when you've some of your boys behind you!"

"A sorry sight, sir," said a seedy-looking man, "these hooligans are putting us all to shame."

But already the Captain was elbowing his way from the scene. There was more than "hooliganism" here: these men meant business. He must extricate himself, and report to the nearest military. He wished, most fervently, that he'd brought his revolver with him.

* * *

What started it all? was to be the cry overseas? Just why should a city, regarded as being as much a part of the United Kingdom as Edinburgh or Cardiff, find itself confronted overnight by Civil War? The answers were not obvious. Not at the time.

At the beginning of the century that was to see her emerge, through blood and tears, as independent of the sister isle, Ireland had never appeared to be in less mood for change. For eight hundred years she had lived under the control of the English, with reactions that had alternated between cowed apathy, fierce revolt and, at times, an almost amused exasperation. The battles against the Anglo-Normans . . . the to-hell-or-Connaught dictum of Cromwell, driving all who resisted from the fertile east and midlands to misery in the poverty-stricken west . . . the rebellion of '98 and the Act of Union that finished the Anglo-Irish Dublin parliament, limited though it was in scope, and corrupt in method . . . the backcloth of the English-Irish relationship had been one that was almost unbelievably sombre. But, with the advent of the twentieth century, happier times seemed on the verge of dawning, and Irishmen had turned out in their hundreds of thousands to give loyal welcome to the visiting Edward VII. It was, by any reckoning, an extraordinary transformation.

Only seventy years before the fêting of His Majesty, the Potato Famine had plunged the nation into horrors that, even now, it is difficult to appreciate. Over one million Irish had been left to die. Over one million more had been forced to emigrate. Appeals to the authorities for justice had done no good at all. There was still enough food in Ireland to have fed its people: the absentee landlords had it exported for profit. A plea to Westminster to impose a temporary ban on shipments had been met by the reply that such a measure would constitute an " unwarrantable interference with the course of Trade." By the turn of the century, however, few Englishmen would have dared defend this rigid extension of Malthusian doctrine. True that the Fenian conspiracy had been toughly—it was thought decisively—suppressed. True also that the nation had experienced the dragging torment of the Land War, and the miseries of eviction. But the administration had turned from force to persuasion to secure the people's loyalty; with paternalistic attempts to remedy past neglect.

Co-operative creameries, subsidies for agriculture, a model system of housing—though a pity that such measures had come so late in the day—the future looked increasingly fair. An Irish middle-class was rapidly establishing itself. An aristocracy—mixed anglo-norman and gael—that was both glitteringly talented and deplorably fickle, and remote from the people forced to endure its whims, had become as near-responsible as an aristocracy can be. Even the religious issue had become less menacing—except perhaps among the extremist Orangemen. Roman Catholic priests were entertained by—and in turn, entertained—Resident Magistrates who were Protestant to a man. In Westminster, over one hundred Irish members struck a balance that neither of the established major parties dare ignore. Among the English public, callous indifference towards their neighbour was giving way to a sense of exaggerated guilt. Yet already, over this encouraging landscape the clouds were once more beginning to build up.

One was the formation of Arthur Griffith's Sinn Fein movement, with ideas for an Ireland completely independent; except perhaps for an acknowledgment of the King, as King of Ireland.

The other was the resistance of the English Conservatives and of the Irish Unionists even to the limited Home Rule demands made by Redmond, leader of the Irish Party in Westminster.

*   *   *

By 1910, Home Rule was on the Statute Book—late in the day, but better late than never; and promised the Irish members at Westminster by a Liberal Government too weak to exist without their support. The Conservatives opposed the measure, and the Protestant North rebelled. Soon the world was confronted by the extraordinary spectacle of Sir Edward Carson—Dublin born it is sometimes forgotten—raising and arming the "rebel" Ulster Volunteers, to resist what they called "treason" to their historic ties with Britain. And then came alarming reports from the Curragh of Kildare, the "Aldershot" of Ireland: the army could not be relied upon to curb him.

Faced with this dilemma, the Government wobbled; and started to back-pedal, with indecent haste. One man alone stood firm, the young and impetuous Winston Churchill. But his own particular brand of "firmness" frightened his colleagues even more. It was claimed that he was in favour of the Navy bombarding Belfast!

The Ulster Volunteers remained in arms. The Home Rule pledge looked like being put on the shelf.

What the Government in Westminster overlooked, in its natural anxiety to avoid a threatened civil war, was the dangerous precedent it was creating in its apparent appeasement of Carson. Having allowed one "private army" to defy it in the North, how could it take exception to private armies in the South?

* * *

It is almost an article of faith in English schoolrooms and often credited in Ireland too, that it was indignation at the Orange success—indignation and fear—that provoked the South to arm. But Carson's move—and the British failure to react to it—was *welcomed* by at least one super-nationalist group. The plotters of the feared and powerful Irish Republican Brotherhood: the American-based secret society known as the I.R.B.

Over the past six years the Brotherhood's agents had been patiently burrowing into the structure of the new Sinn Fein movement, seeking to exploit the romantic nationalism it generated—with its emphasis on Gaelic "separateness"—and divert its policy of non-co-operation with the British administration into more violent channels. To these dedicated descendants of the Fenians, the Ulster crisis and the strong feelings it aroused was heaven-sent. In a Volunteer force they could at last have the army that was an essential to their plans for revolution. All that they had to do was to find the man who—unknowingly—could serve as "front", and thus conceal the purpose they had in mind for such a force. They found him quite quickly, and by accident.

An article had appeared in a publication that specialised in nationalist appeal of the "language" variety. Headed "The North Began" it not only hotly attacked the Government for giving way to Carson but urged that, as Ulster now threatened Home Rule with armed force, the South should have armed force with which to defend it. If the Unionists could raise their private army, why shouldn't the Nationalists do likewise?

The I.R.B. were delighted by this plea, and the widespread interest it aroused. Equally were they amazed at the identity of the author—the precise, tidy-minded, and highly respected Eoin MacNeill.

MacNeill, the acknowledged authority on the Irish language, and with friends throughout Dublin's intellectual society, was the last man to be suspected by the Castle of plotting revolutionary violence. Professor of Ancient History in University College, a former top civil servant, and leaning politically towards the Irish (parliamentary) party, his impeccable respectability would attract to a Volunteer force thousands who at that stage would not have touched republicanism with a barge-pole.

The Brotherhood were correct in their assessment. Formed under MacNeill's innocent aegis—he was made their President —the Irish Volunteers recruited 15,000 men in a matter of weeks. But what the majority of the 15,000 did not realise —and neither did MacNeill—was that the effective control of this "defensive" force was to all intents and purposes in the hands of republican extremists.

For this amazing takeover—its cool effrontery unprecedented in history—two men were primarily responsible: one of them a semi-invalid, veteran of English jails, and the other a tough barman: on the surface, neither of them looked a very likely hero.

*   *   *

It was in 1907 when a sparsely built and somewhat seedy looking little man, with pale rather watery eyes and a greying moustache returned quietly and unobtrusively to the land to which he had dedicated his life; and the lives of others too.

Although regarded by the Government of Ireland as an inciter of the dynamiteer and assassin, and revered in I.R.B.

26

circles as a veteran of the Fenians, Thomas J. Clarke was, in appearance, neither sinister or heroic. His rather scraggy neck, with its prominent adam's apple, projecting from a winged collar that always seemed a size too large . . . the sparse hair that fluffed out around his bald and crinkled crown . . . his air of almost timid curiosity . . . these combined to give him a rather appealing aspect; reminiscent of a slightly moulting sparrow. He lived frugally, and had none of the stock vices. He was teetotal, and mild-spoken, and kept his eyes off the women. He was also the trusted lieutenant of the Brotherhood's secret boss: James Devoy, controlling affairs from America.

By the time he was fifty, Thomas Clarke had spent over a third of his life in English jails. His wasted body bore the scars. So did his angry brain. He had been in "exile" in New York when Devoy had summoned him. He had been sent back to Ireland with a specific directive. Ireland, it was feared had become complacent: and the Brotherhood in Ireland was in danger of extinction; the victim, on this occasion, not so much of English "tyranny", but of public apathy created by English "kindness". Where the dragoons and the police had consistently failed, the Birrell regime looked remarkably like succeeding: it was up to Clarke to insure that it did not.

After six years of not very conspicuous success—his infiltration of the Sinn Fein movement was necessarily discreet—Clarke latched on to the Carson affair like a castaway to a lifebelt. Once the volunteers were launched he at last could see land in sight.

The Brotherhood went into action with superlative skill. Already, by ostensibly associating himself with the aspirations of Sinn Fein, Clarke had made many contacts among the intellectuals, and carefully noted those who were likely to support future direct action. Now, in collecting funds throughout the countryside for the burgeoning Volunteers, he got to know his men even better. As also did Sean McDermott, his fellow I.R.B. agent.

With his handsome appearance, and fiery eloquence, this former barman seemed a splendid asset to the Volunteer movement. The success of his recruiting speeches—plus his judicious plugging by the Brotherhood's secret supporters —soon placed him among the hierarchy, and in a key position. He was given the task of officer selection: needless to say he chose extremists.

By 1914 the "committee" that governed the activities of the volunteers had no fewer than four of Clarke's nominees in its membership of twelve. Padraic Pearse . . . Thomas McDonagh . . . Edmond Kent . . . McDermott himself . . . each was a full member of the I.R.B. . . . each exerted a tremendous influence . . . and all of them were pledged to launch, at the opportune time, an attack in arms against the "Saxon Foe."

It was then, however, when they were cementing their hold on a force that was growing from day to day more radical, that the plans of the Brotherhood received an unexpected setback. John Redmond took over.

* * *

Leader of the Irish party at Westminster, Redmond had come to regard the volunteers with concern. Ostensibly, the movement's aims still ran parallel with his own. It was pledged to defend against aggression the Home Rule principle, of which he was the parliamentary exponent. No fool however, he could see in its association with Sinn Fein and the radical spirit abroad among its junior officers, not so much an auxiliary and ally but a rival to the Party. Now —"out of the blue" as it was later complained—he decided to take action. The military arm must come under the party's civilian control: if it did not, he would throw all his weight into denouncing it.

This intervention was a terrific blow to the aspirations of the republicans; but protest as much as they liked, they had to give way. Into the committee whose "takeover" had been so brilliantly achieved, the party now planted its own nominees and watchdogs. The Brotherhood had to bide its time.

The public standing of the Irish Volunteers dramatically increased. In prestige and numbers, they were soon second to none. On paper at least, their membership increased to 150,000, and as it did so the I.R.B. could feel its own influence declining. And then, as a bonus—or restorative for the Brotherhood—came the War.

Carried away by the prevailing enthusiasm, and possibly each with an eye to future advantage for his cause, Carson and Redmond offered a truce on the Home Rule issue until hostilities were over; the latter even declaring, in a typically emotional outburst, that the volunteers themselves would defend Ireland from the Germans.

Immediately the Brotherhood pounced. The Redmond promise—widely applauded though it was by an overwrought House and country—was challenged and denounced.

Redmond—the I.R.B. agents were prompt to point out—had no authority to pledge the movement to any major line of policy: let alone what amounted to an alliance with England. He must retract.

Furious at the hostility that he could sense had been built up by McDermott, confident in his great popularity with the mass of the rank and file, and extremely jealous of his prestige as political leader, Redmond struck back.

In a determined effort to break the opposition once for all, he chose the little town of Woodenbridge, near to his birthplace, for the delivery of a policy speech that went far further than anything he had yet said in the Commons. He urged all Irishmen not only to defend their island, but to join the British army, as a point of honour and expediency, and to sink all differences until victory was won.

It was a speech that was to mark the parting of the ways.

At a snap emergency meeting the Committee "expelled" Redmond's men, and denounced his leadership. Redmond, in turn, denounced the Committee and "seceded"—and nine tenths of the volunteers seceded too. They formed a new organisation, the National Volunteers.

*   *   *

A foreign military observer visiting Ireland in 1916 would have found plenty to observe, and much to confuse.

He would have seen four private armies, each at loggerheads with each other, marching, counter-marching and carrying out manoeuvres on the soil which each regarded as exclusively its own and to which each pledged its devotion to the death. And in between these bewildering comings and goings he would doubtless have noted the strictly neutral and see-no-evil stance maintained by yet a fifth force: the British Army in Ireland, with its Connaughts, Leinsters, Inniskillings and the rest, as Irish in its content as any of the others and backed by a plethora of cadet forces, privately raised auxiliaries, and the armed police of the R.I.C.

Had the observer enquired into the composition of these forces, raised in an island whose total population was slightly less than half that of London, he would have discovered that the Ulster Volunteers, opposing Home Rule, and the National Volunteers, supporting it, were about evenly matched in numbers; totalling between them nearly a third of a million men.

In contrast with such an impressive tally, the "extremist" forces looked very small beer indeed.

The Irish Volunteers now had a turn out of less than 10,000 —one eighteenth of the strength they could muster at the time of Redmond's withdrawal.

Connolly's Citizen Army was, in numbers, a joke. Even at the height of the great labour disputes that had convulsed pre-war Dublin and caused 30,000 strikers to clash in bitter battle with the police, its membership had totalled only 250. In 1916 it was even less than that.

What was ignored however by those who—inhibited by their previous failure to act against the larger groups—refused to take action against these "extremist" minorities was the latter's strong sense of purpose, discipline and dedication.

This oversight was to cost the authorities dear.

*   *   *

As copies of the Proclamation—run off the presses at Liberty Hall—were being fixed by the rebels to the Nelson Pillar and the first shots were being fired in the Castle and along the waterfront, a stocky little man with an aggressively outsize moustache was working at his home in Clontarff, and congratulating himself that the Rising had been called off. Armed conflict, he was convinced, could end only with English victory, and the wreck of that very cause—Ireland a Nation!—which he, perhaps more than any other man, had helped to grow and prosper.

At 44, Arthur Griffiths was revered in nationalist circles as the man whose cry of Sinn Fein had re-awakened, and given new strength to, a national consciousness enfeebled and sunk in apathy. To quote one leading authority of the time, "he called us from our mourning at the Cenotaph of Ireland's hopes—Parnell's grave at Glasnevin—and showed us there was work that we, the living, must do."

Untidy, and good hearted, a tireless and enthusiastic walker and talker, a man who wanted nothing for himself, but everything for the propagation of his beliefs and teaching, Griffith was probably the most unexpected genius ever to have been produced by Ireland, traditionally the source of the unlikely and unexpected.

Despite his lack of stature—he was under five foot four —Arthur Griffith, on leaving school, had an athletic record that more robust types would have envied. He was a high-jumper, a weight-thrower, a lover of every type of sport. By 1916, despite his shyness, air of absent-mindedness, and the kindliness of the grey-blue eyes that so belied the militant ferocity of the luxuriance over his lip, he had proved himself possessed of a strength of will and consistency of motive that, until his emergence, the intellectual strata of the resistance to rule from England had all too conspicuously lacked.

Together with William Rooney, who wrote all night and toiled all day on the wharfside, it was Griffith who founded the United Irishman, soon the voice of the Gaelic League, with its emphasis on a "separate culture", and separateness through language from the anglo-saxon. Later his ideas developed a stage further. Passionately he pointed to the example of Hungary as the key to Ireland's salvation. Separate language . . . separate culture . . . separate parliaments . . . a dual monarchy if need be!

To most men the results of this effort would have been discouraging. The United Irishman was twenty times seized by the police. Three times it was suppressed. But still Griffith pursued his stormy petrel course. W. B. Yeats, George Russell (AE) and "John Eglinton" became contributors to his much harassed journal.

It was not until 1905 however that Griffith first used the title that was to rally the forces of the new-type nationalism and—misinterpreted—used to cover every activity directed at British rule in Ireland.

Griffith was complaining to a supporter, the beautiful Mary Ellen Butler, the difficulty of expressing in a simple phrase his policy of self-sufficiency, and "separateness" from the sister culture.

"Then what about Sinn Fein (ourselves)?" Miss Butler asked.

"Sinn Fein," cried Griffith delightedly. "Exactly the words I want!"

Sinn Fein it was.

The first convention of the National Council of the new movement took place in a shabby room in the old Rotunda of Dublin on November 28th, 1905. Less than a hundred men, and a handful of women and girls, took the trouble to attend. But Griffith steadfastly refused to be discouraged.

"You have too lofty an opinion of the people's future," a friend protested. "They have been too long in slavery to show the moral courage which your policy demands."

Said Griffith elatedly "I am not concerned about today, for tomorrow will be ours . . ."

There were no half-measures about the apostle of the creed of Ireland for the Irish. He fought the weight of Government with his theories of passive resistance and non-co-operation. He also fought a retired pork butcher, who had "snapped up" the sacred Hill of Tara in the hope of unearthing its treasures. He wore clothes that were made in Ireland, shoes that were made in Ireland, worked on a desk that was made in Ireland, and ate only food that was produced in Ireland. Even the tobacco that filled his pipe was Irish—a compound of herbs, it's said, that created consternation among his friends.

Yet, the greater his dedication to the "Cause", the more careless he became about his health and comfort. He was deplorably untidy, worked all hours of day and night, and was the prey of every sponger clinging to the movement's cloak. Thus, when Griffith married, his friends breathed deep and heartfelt sighs of affection and relief. At least the "master" would be properly looked after. And, though he had persistently refused help for himself, surely he could not refuse it for his wife.

They bought him a house.

Arthur Griffith expressed his gratitude, with tears in his eyes at their kindness. But, at the same time, deplored the thougthlessness of it.

"I have married," he protested, "the best girl in the world. We would be happy anywhere. And now you have to do this! If you'd given me the money instead, I could have ploughed it back into my journal, and helped the movement forward."

"It was," he said, "a waste."

Soon afterwards the house was sold, the movement received fresh funds, and Mr and Mrs Griffith were conducting their devoted fight from "digs."

Such was the man who, on rebellion's eve, the new leader of the Volunteers had chosen deliberately to mislead and isolate.

It was the climax to a split within the movement that had almost wrecked the rising before it started.

* * *

Unbeknown to MacNeill. Unbeknown to Griffith. Unbeknown to all but a handful of plotters, a decision had been made to launch an insurrection as far back as September 1914—and the Brotherhood had "authorised" an attempt to seek German aid!

It was an incredible piece of arrogance, this almost contemptuous by-passing of the volunteer leadership. All the same, it was necessary; essential even. MacNeill had been useful enough as a respectable "front", but, much though Pearse and the other I.R.B. nominees respected him for his personal integrity and perhaps hitherto unsuspected strength of character, his very virtues threatened to become embarrassing obstacles.

By 1915, the Brotherhood's directors in America had become impatient for results. Was not England's difficulty Ireland's opportunity? And what better time to fight, than when one had a strong ally at one's side? MacNeill however was known to be completely opposed to any military action, except in self-defence. It would be fatal to give him the slightest hint of German alliance. Care was needed.

It was during these months of waiting and plotting—and skilful "planting" of republican militants in units that might be considered "unreliable"—that Pearse and his friends were relieved to notice that MacNeill was becoming more and more divorced from the daily life of the movement. The prospects of immediate crisis with the North diminishing, he was content to return for long periods to his beloved books, and his enthusiasm for the Gaelic in the academic sense. Just as well.

Since 1914 that strange and complex figure, Sir Roger Casement had been busy in Germany, fostering the I.R.B.'s ally. He had got small change. For months on end he had stomped the prison camps that housed thousands of Irish p.o.w.'s, and had offered them the strongest inducements to join the force that was to "liberate" their country. An Irish Brigade.

Alas for Sir Roger.

All that he succeeded in collecting was abuse, volleys of stones, shouts of "hang the traitor" and the exasperation of the disappointed "ally". Even the mere handful of Irishmen who did rally to his call, delivered with the sincerity and passion—and blind misunderstanding of human everyday reactions—that characterised him in his role of dedicated nationalist, had to be disbanded. The Germans no longer would agree to take them seriously.

"Of course," he wrote to a colleague with sad frankness, "it isn't an Irish *Brigade*—that is the trouble. It is merely a handful of men who have volunteered, and their numbers are so few they can not be recognised, and the authorities do not see their way to deal with them as if they were a real military force. With only 55 men, all told, we lay ourselves open to ridicule and contempt, and instead of doing Ireland good, we shall injure our cause and help Redmond and the traitors . . ."

This fact accepted, Sir Roger attempted to find another way of "helping". Get guns, and machine guns, and rifles and hand grenades for the use of the Irish in Ireland; and if possible land *German* troops to support them. The Kaiser's military advisers looked at the map, the sea thereon, and then at Sir Roger—and despaired. In the meanwhile however they kept their thoughts to themselves. It had been decided to send some form of limited aid, to keep the Irish battle on the boil for cynically political purposes; but Sir Roger need not know that.

Nor need he know just yet that the Irish Republican Brotherhood, losing faith completely in the adventures of Ireland's eccentric missionary, had sent a representative of their own to negotiate behind his back. Already they had fixed the date of the rising. Easter Sunday.

* * *

MacNeill called on Pearse, engaged in the usual civilities, and then said almost apologetically: "I hear rumours of an insurrection being planned. There's no truth in this nonsense, is there?"

"Good heavens, no!" the other managed to choke out.

Happy with the reassurance the Volunteer Chief of Staff returned to his studies.

"All the same, a close shave," said the I.R.B. man to his colleagues. Had he but known it, there was an even closer shave to come.

The departure for Ireland of the German auxiliary cruiser *Libau*, under the guise of a Norwegian tramp steamer, the *Aud*, and her capture by the Royal Navy and consequent scuttling has often been told. So also has the story of the arrest of Roger Casement, landed by submarine a few hours before. This followed—a fact that has since been accepted even by those who at the time were foremost in demanding his execution as a traitor—his personal and complete disillusionment with the German "ally". At last aware of the I.R.B. negotiations, and the fact that the date of the rising had been fixed, Casement was both shocked by what he regarded as double-dealing, and appalled by the paucity of German aid. No artillery could be provided. Not one German technician. Only 20 machine guns and 20,000 rifles, of Russian make; captured on the Eastern front. So badly did he feel about this, it's said today, that, far from intending to take a leading role in the battle, his tragic trip to Ireland was made in the effort to stop it starting: the German arms could be saved for a more propitious day. But the most astonishing aspect of all about those truly astonishing and all-critical

34

days before Easter is that the departure date of the *Aud*, and that of Casement too, was known to British Naval Intelligence, and passed on to the Irish authorities. Without the latter appreciating their significance or urgency.

The news of the *Aud*'s sailing alerted forty British warships. It had been obtained by Naval Intelligence under the leadership of the renowned Sir Reginald Hall—opponent of the German master spy von Rintelen. Sir Reginald's men had broken down the German cypher, and intercepted the traffic between Germany and the German Embassy in Washington, the clearing house for communications between the I.R.B. and their allies. Yet this striking coup's effect was to be negatived by subsequent neglect. The transcript of the information was sent via the army's Irish Command to Nathan, without any priority rating to distinguish it immediately from the other "bumph" with which the Castle was so liberally provided. Only after Casement's arrest did light dawn upon the bureaucrats in Dublin.

Among the Volunteers that arrest created something approaching panic.

* * *

Pearse decided it was now or never. While the Castle was deliberating on when to act and how—and Nathan was urging further delays on the grounds that, after the *Aud* sinking, the rebels would not be "mad" enough to rise—Pearse had made up his mind that to wait would be suicide. He decided to have it out with MacNeill, once and for all.

There had been an unpleasant scene at his home only twenty-four hours before. Officers of Volunteer commands in the provinces had informed MacNeill of the orders to stage the rising—under the guise of manoeuvres—and had given him the date. MacNeill had promptly dashed over to see Pearse; and raised Hell. He would not tolerate for a moment such a mad enterprise, with its certain toll among the Volunteers. Resolutely, though outwardly submissive, Pearse had decided to go ahead. But he knew—with sinking heart —what this could entail. MacNeill's influence could halve the already scant force available.

That I.R.B. stalwart MacDermott then decided to intervene, and had gone to the President with strong words of warning. He had pointed out that the arms ship was on its way; nothing could now stop the rising from starting. The Volunteer movement was committed: there could be no turning back. The landing of the arms would be the signal for authority to strike at the movement. Mass arrests and suppression would follow as surely as night followed day.

It was a grim picture he unfolded: of certain conflict and, if MacNeill did not change his mind, certain defeat. At last the leader had capitulated. "If we have to fight or be suppressed," he said, "then I'm ready to fight."

But what would MacNeil's reactions be now that *this* had happened? The loss of the arms . . . the arrest of Casement . . . it seemed that the British were privy to all their plans. Which way would MacNeill jump now?

It was not long before he got his answer. After yet another stormy interview—with both men shouting at each other in anger—MacNeill handed to O'Rahilly, tough, determined and one of his most staunch supporters, an order which he was to distribute through all commands. It read:

"Volunteers completely deceived. All orders for special action are hereby cancelled and on no account will action be taken."

Then to make certainty doubly sure, MacNeill pedalled over to the Sunday Independent and saw the editor. Soon that paper was carrying what was later to be known as The Countermanding Order.

"Owing to the very critical position, all orders given to the Irish Volunteers for tomorrow, Easter Sunday, are hereby rescinded and no parades, marches, or other movement of Irish Volunteers will take place. Each individual Volunteer will obey this order strictly and in every particular."

The news broke like a bombshell on the conference of officers—and their allies of the Citizen Army. They had never expected the Chief to take the initiative so decisively, and history might have taken a different course if vehemently angry James Connolly had not been there to restore their damaged morale. "If we don't fight now," roared Connolly, "all that we have to hope and pray for is that an earthquake will swallow Ireland up!"

In defiance of MacNeill—and cold-shouldering Arthur Griffith—the fateful decision was reached. The insurrection would go ahead as planned, but with the date altered to Monday.

Almost as an afterthought, it was then decided to "expel" the President. MacNeill's place henceforward would be held by Padraic Pearse.

*   *   *

In O'Connell Street the crowds continued to grow. The

police were withdrawn from central Dublin—already three of these unarmed men had been shot, and the Commissioner was taking no more chances.

Priests now gathered from a nearby seminary, and formed a cordon which swept down the street, trying to push the crowd ahead of it: trying to disperse it: trying in the name of Easter to urge all men to peace. But as fast as the people fell back in one section, the greater grew their pressure on another. There was laughter, jeers at the rebels, a little applause here and there, the singing of "God Save Ireland" by a few patriots and drunks. And still the crowd grew.

But suddenly, on its fringes, there came signs of dispersal, and scattered shouts that became a frightening yell.

"The Lancers are coming . . . the Lancers!"

The crowd broke into fragments, fleeing for shelter before nameless, long-inherited fears.

CHAPTER THREE

Sent into the city on the initiative of the Viceroy himself
—so it was rumoured at the time—the Lancers approached
O'Connell Street at a seemingly effortless trot, and with an
outward air of almost sublime assurance.

All the way from their quarters, in Marlborough Barracks,
Phoenix Park, they had been subject to the admiring gaze and
occasional applause of crowds who were still blissfully
unaware of the purpose of the ride: many thinking it was a
sort of holiday entertainment.

Framed by their upright lances, pennants stirring, the
straight-backed, tight-jacketed cavalrymen, rising and falling
only slightly to the sway of their glittering saddles, suggested
to Mrs Sarah Spellman—hurrying home to entertain friends
expected from the country—a picture that was almost
medieval. To others, the metallic ring of hooves and lively
jingle of rein and bit, recalled the pre-war pleasantries of a
musical ride. But now, as the Lancers neared O'Connell Street,
and the guilty witnesses of its rebellious goings-on fled into
the side-streets, the cavalcade evoked, among those few who
remained to stare, associations of a vastly different sort.

Years later, a loyalist old soldier—once a cavalryman
himself—was to say: "There was I, all ready to cheer the
column, when suddenly—you'll hardly believe it—I felt like
a bloody shinner!"

It was as though, when seen from the kerbside "the old
regiment had completely changed its face". The troopers took
their mastery so much for granted, he explained, "that the
sight of them tore at one's pride. When I saw the bloody
crowd scatter, and run like rabbits before them, I felt almost
ashamed of being Irish!"

More clear-cut perhaps are the recollections of an insurgent
rifleman. "We had them in our sights all the way," he recalls,
"and they must damn well have known it. Yet not one of
those fellows ever turned a hair. Sure, it was just as though
they couldn't believe we would have the *cheek* to pull
trigger . . ."

The squadron cantered towards the north entrance to the
street. There was no variation in the rhythm of its brisk
advance. No attempt at deployment. The men continued to

look steadily to their front. There was no sign of excitement. Even the panic of the scattering crowd, and the sight of sandbags sagging from the windows of a restaurant, did not divert the van of the cavalcade from its parade ground approach. And then, as the main body came into view, the silence of those who watched was broken by a universal sigh.

It was a sigh of expectancy, fascination and near-grief. It was followed immediately by shrill shouts of warning.

The officer leading the Lancers swung lithely in his saddle. He glanced briefly at the onlookers, then at the rooftops, and turned to say something to the sergeant riding close behind him. But otherwise there was no sign of interest. It was as if the squadron were dumb and blind and deaf. Pennants still fluttered proudly. Carbines remained in their buckets. Brass buttons and nutbrown leather winked gaily at the sun.

"Look out for yourselves," the old soldier found himself crying. "Look out for yourselves—the bowsies will mow you down!"

It was only when it had reached a point just north of the Parnell Monument that the squadron deployed from column, fanned out across the street, and with well-drilled precision came to a halt. A strange hush wrapped the street: like the silence before the storm. For a moment the officer stared hard-faced at the Post Office, and the two strange flags that flew above its portico, and then transferred his gaze to the white and black copies of the Proclamation, flaunting themselves around the base of Nelson's Pillar, and the tram that lay overturned a few yards beyond it. It was a moment of apparent indecision, with an outcome decided solely by blind chance.

The arrival of the Lancers had confused and confounded a detachment of volunteers, about to cross the street to join their comrades in the Post Office. But now, with the horsemen halted, they decided to make a rush for it.

At sight of the running men, the officer stiffened. He raised his arm full length, and a naked sword flashed in the sun. A brisk command preceded sudden movement among the troopers. The unreal calm was shattered by the thunder of the charge.

* * *

Instinct asserting itself, the old soldier ran for cover. He fell into a shop doorway, hurling himself to the floor. And, as he did so, the reaction of the Post Office garrison fell upon the cheering horsemen like a hammer.

* * *

It came with a fusilade from fifty rifles or more—a fusilade that, at point-blank range, ripped into the proud squadron and tore it into pieces. In seconds, the splendid pageant had dissolved into so many separate fragments, each of them one of agony.

Troop horses whinnied, slipped and slithered and fell. Their riders rolled with them, to be pinned beneath their weight. Hands clutched—too late—at the butts of still-sheathed carbines. The storm of fire from the Howth mausers scattered and shattered a wild attempt to close.

Inside the Post Office, an exultant Connolly, grabbed a rifle himself, and joined in the shooting. Below him, the khaki mass milled hopelessly over the tramlines. It seemed that the Lancers were on the verge of rout.

"More! More!" he yelled to his young riflemen.

One man kept his head in the chaos of the street. The man who, under orders, had led the squadron into its baited trap.

" 'A' squadron!"

The officer's shout somehow steadied the riders. Near-panic eased at the assured note of authority, and the sight of him, erect as ever in his saddle, despite the bullets that flew like angry bees around his head. Briefly he glanced at the Post Office, and then towards the dead.

" 'A' Squadron will retire . . ."

The horsemen reformed north of the Parnell monument, and then began to move towards the place from whence they came. Almost miraculously, the bulk of them arrived there.

Over-excitement on the part of the rebels? Excitement so intense that it caused them to miss their aim? Or had the initial carnage so shocked the raw volunteers that it had left some of them unwilling to finish the job they had started?

To this day, the escape of the Lancers from what should have been their annihilation has never been satisfactorily explained. It remains as much a subject for speculation and criticism as the fantastically unreal parade that preceded it, or the hopelessly wild shooting that after the first volley, killed rebel snipers on the other side of the street.

* * *

While the fierce fusilade in O'Connell Street marked

Dublin's first real awakening to the realities of revolt, the Lancers were also in trouble near the Northern Quays.

At this point the embankment on the northern side of the Liffey was dominated by the rebel-held Four Courts—its imposing cupola now flaunting the tricolour, and occupied by snipers—and a number of hurriedly fortified buildings on its flanks. The area, which included the notorious Bachelor's Walk—scene of the bloody skirmish between the Howth gun-runners and the Scottish Borderers twenty-two months previously—was noted for its extreme nationalist sympathies. It was occupied by Daly's 1st Dublin Battalion, one of the most efficient volunteer units to take the field. This latter fact, however, the military were to learn the hard way.

In the early hours of Monday, a consignment of ammunition had arrived at North Wall Station, and a troop of cavalry had been detailed to escort it through the city to Phoenix Park. Like so many other aspects of the rebellion, the purpose of this move is still somewhat of a mystery. At the time, British communiques referred to the amount of the ammunition involved as "small". In actual fact, it filled no fewer than six wagons. Laconically, its dispatch was claimed to be a matter of "routine". The author has heard a vastly different story.

According to this, both the dispatch of the ammunition and the decision to guard it, stemmed from the desire of Friend and his colleagues to insure against trouble when, after the holidays, they started to deal with the Sinn Fein leadership.

If this be so, then it certainly reflects to the credit of that oft-criticised General's foresight, and makes it seem even more of a pity—from the British point of view—that the Lancers, on Easter Monday, were to prove to be accident-prone.

"Alice in Wonderland" a senior officer has since described the decision to route the convoy through the quays at a time when it was known that the city was in disturbance. It was to have a rougher tag from those condemned to endure its bitter consequences.

* * *

The approach of the troopers, and the wagon train trundling between them, was greeted with incredulity by the locals and consternation on the part of the police. Didn't the lancers know they were riding into an area where the Volunteers were out in strength? The officer commanding shrugged the warnings aside. He had his orders, and was determined to carry them out. The convoy was in sight of the Four Courts when it was halted by yet another well-intentioned plea to turn back. Impatiently, the officer ordered his men to continue their advance.

The range had closed to a hundred yards when the insurgents released safety-catches. Then, at a shouted command, they let fly at the cavalry with everything they'd got.

Eight lancers fell in little more than twenty seconds. Disorganised, a few riders charged up King Street, came under fire and were forced to ride back again. The bullets seemed to come from all directions. Yet here—as at the Post Office—the consequences of the military's outrageous over-confidence were part redeemed by their courage and good discipline.

Young Lieutenant Hudson rallied the men around the wagons, and viciously, despite the odds against them, the Lancers began to shoot back. Instead of abandoning the convoy in a wild stampede for safety they covered its retreat into nearby Charles Street. And there they holed-up, refusing surrender terms and answering a flag of truce with a volley from their carbines.

Littering the road along the quayside lay the bodies of their comrades. Riderless horses, maddened with wounds and fright, careered blindly around the Four Courts in a lather of sweat and blood. The insurgents secured a tricolour to a captured lance and planted it outside a nearby pub. The place was later to gain fame as Riley's Fort.

*　　*　　*

Amid the sprawling rooftops and battlements of Dublin Castle, with its eccentricities of architecture ranging from Norman to Victorian, the little garrison still waited breathlessly for the rebel attack to be resumed, and pressed home. Heroic defiance was the order of the day: drama had all the participants in its grip. Nathan prepared a dispatch, though no one seemed to know how it could be delivered. Ostentatiously, and incongruously, a loaded revolver lay on the desk beside him.

"Will he kill himself, if they take over . . ." queried an awed civil servant.

The setting was productive of such emotional speculation.

Barring the approach from Castle Yard, a section of the detachment from Ship Street Barracks waited with rifles

42

trained on the rebel-held guardroom, while their comrades, among them marksmen placed in the old Norman Berming-ham Tower, swapped shots with rebel snipers installed in the City Hall. ·

Civil servants nervously fingered unfamiliar weapons, encouraged by elderly aides nostalgic for battles long since past.

In the gilded splendour of St Patrick's Hall—where they had been moved for greater safety than that afforded by the Castle's hospital ward—the wounded chafed and fumed at their inability to get at "the bloody shinners", while young nurses kept a sort of desperate calm; wishing that they too could bears arms like men.

Captain Price, rather pleased with having been able to christen his revolver, and the sergeant of the detachment from Ship Street, *not* so pleased at the criticisms levelled over the capture of the guardroom, had become, in this mixed bag of innocents besieged, the sole repositories of military know-how.

And now, in the Captain's temporary absence—as he attended Nathan and attempted futilely to send appeals for aid across a tangle of severed phone lines—it was to the Sergeant and his men that all turned with a new and wondrous respect.

For their part, the Ship Street men anticipated an immediate attack. The rebels, they reckoned, would attempt to snatch the prize before reinforcements could reach it. They would risk—*must* risk—a rush while the going was good. Like most others in the Castle, the soldiers visualised an enemy numbered in hordes: they saw no reason why he should long hold back.

Bullets were ripping through the cobbles of the Yard or ringing the changes on the chimney pots. In general, the fire was wild; but there was accurate sniping too. Parts of the square ·beyond the guardroom became death traps for those who crossed. There was a constant cry of "Stretcher Bearers".

"Softening us up," said the Sergeant with reminiscent gloom, "but we'll give them a bloody nose before they do us!"

Yet, after half an hour of this rifle barrage, even Price and he began to show puzzlement and uncertainty. It seemed almost inexplicable—this failure of the rebels to follow up their early advantage—for the soldiers had few illusions as to what would happen if they did.

Price had twenty-one young regulars and a handful of civilians available to defend this warren of courtyards, government offices, and state apartments. Twenty-one young regulars and a handful of civilians with which to defend a complex spread for over twenty acres and more! "About time they made their minds up," muttered the Sergeant irritably, "and about time *our* side did something about it too." For what the hell was happening to the troops in the city? Where were the columns that should have come to the Castle's relief?

*　　*　　*

The news of the cavalry's humiliating reverses, and the successful storming of the Castle's guardroom, quickly spread among the volunteer strongpoints in all sections of the city, and—magnified en route—did much for morale. These skirmishes, it was said, had shown that the British had lost their stomach for fighting: the descendants of the victors of Vinegar Hill could be outclassed and outfought by the "corner boys" they had so often held up to derision. The air was heady, dangerously so. No one appears to have appreciated that the "enemy" guards had had no live ammunition with which to resist their capture. Nor was there criticism of the failure to follow up the initial advantage. The mood of the hour was one of unquestioning optimism: eyes were blind to the portents of subsequent disillusion.

In St Stephen's Green, it was said the Countess wept with pride when she heard of the fight near the Four Courts. At H.Q.—when the Lancers withdrew—the happy rebels sang The Soldiers Song. Near Jacob's Biscuit Factory, this latter news was welcomed by that modest author Patrick Kearney. *His* day had otherwise lacked romantic overtones.

At the G.P.O. the garrison could well indulge in self-satisfaction. They had not only engaged the foe: they had contributed to the making of military-political history. For surely never before had there been such a war as this—where the first serious engagement had been decided on the doorstep of the Government that declared it! And where else but in Ireland could you possibly have found a Cabinet with the guts to take part in the shooting? However, for Patrick Kearney, such exhilaration was lacking. The circumstances in which he and his mates were working were singularly devoid of martial glory.

Jacob's had been chosen as their area headquarters not only because of its products—biscuits and cakes were to be the insurgents' staple diet—but also because of its positions and great strength. Massively built, six storeys high, the factory provided an excellent vantage-point and a fortress dominating approaches to the Castle from Portobello Bridge, the Canal to the south, and Richmond Barracks to the south-west. But now, as the volunteers laboured to build barricades to block the adjoining streets, the advantages of the place seemed to have been bought too dearly. Each move they made met with nothing but abuse.

"Poor but loyal" had been the motto of the district. Poor but loyal it remained. Its inhabitants had a formidable record of agitation. Against the bosses, strikes, lock-outs and demonstrations came as natural as religion. They had intense and inbred differences with the police, based on incidents dating so far back as to be literally historic. Yet even the combined eloquence of marxist and nationalist agitators had failed to stop them turning out in their thousands to cheer the visit of King Edward. At the time the streets had been festooned by Union Jacks, the only flag they acknowledged, knew and gave their loyalty to. They were rough folk, and frank folk too. "Outrage" was a mild word to describe their feelings about the apostles of rebellion.

"Yez omathauns," screamed a shawlie at the luckless volunteers. "Just wait toll my Johnnie comes home, and he'll teach yez how to soldier!"

"The Tommies'll tan the arse from your bloody Sinn Fein britches," was the charitable prophecy of the shawlie's girl companion.

The bitterness and anger felt by the women was particularly intense, and based on strongly personal motives. Many of them had husbands, sons and sweethearts at the Front—and loyalty was thus fortified by family sentiment. It enjoyed, in addition, an economic stimulus: God help the rebels if they held up separation allowances!

To this background of unwelcome, the would-be liberators endeavoured to block their ears; but, for all that, it was hard to maintain a revolutionary fervour. Nor was Kearney's section alone in experiencing the wrath of their country-women. As they realised from reports from other districts they were lucky not to have to put up with anything worse than the current verbal bombardment. One small detachment of Volunteers had been physically mauled by these true-blue and angry amazons, who had secured though only temporarily, a rifle as their trophy. Another group had been stoned and spat upon: yet another treated to a barrage of rotten vegetables. Such ugly vignettes of what the devotees of nationalism had looked forward to as "Ireland's fight for freedom", and the leaders of the Citizen Army had regarded as the start of militant socialism, were disheartening, to say the least, and Kearney found himself pretty near to tears.

Unlike many of his superiors in the Volunteers the rebel poet had known too much of poverty, and the behaviour state of simple people exposed to unusual stresses, to accept the crowd's attitude as deeply-based or permanent. All the same he reflected—though not resting from his work—it boded ill for Pearse's hopes that the rising would create its own momentum, and snowball into national revolution.

Confidence in the leadership's control of even the most simple tactical dispositions was also on the wane, and, an hour later, almost completely vanished.

"You're to leave the barricade and get back to Jacobs' at once," said the kid on the bike.

"Who says so?"

"Sure, you're wasting your bloody time. It's McDonagh who says so!"

"F . . .!"

It had been decided that the position would not be held. Instead, the outposts would withdraw and reinforce the factory.

The final humiliation for the depressed volunteers came when they marched back to Jacobs', and found it beset by a crowd so formidably hostile that it had sunk even its traditional differences with the peelers. A group of police cadets were egging the women on. Traitors and bastards were the prettiest terms employed . . .

The main entrance to the factory had been locked and barricaded, and the working party had to go in by a narrow wicket gate. They could only do so one at a time, and as Kearney later recorded, "Each one of us got a parting salute from a hand or a foot, whichever was the most convenient for the ladies . . ."

"What a difference," he wryly added, "from youth's ideal of 'see who comes over the red-blossomed heather'."

* * *

The Irish insurgents were not alone in being surprised by the reaction of the people. Nor was it solely the working-class that was to prove itself "more royalist than the king". While Kearney and his comrades were enduring the insults of their countrywomen—"we'll hang the lot of yez, if the British don't do the job!"—units of the Crown Forces, moving rather indecisively into the outer suburbs, were cheered and fêted.

46

Captain Knight—weary and dishevelled after three hours of an adventurous zig-zag through rebel positions all the way from the Nelson Pillar—finally came into grateful contact with a column halted to the west of the Phoenix Park.

Smoking free cigarettes, and surrounded by empty beer bottles the tommies were resting outside a row of fashionable mansions, while the class-kindred of Count Plunkett and the impetuous O'Rahilly ministered to the palates of the officers. Slices of cold chicken were washed down by Moselle.

The mood—Knight felt—was one of holiday, but he derived small comfort from this unexpected discovery. The dreamlike quality he had sensed about the events of the morning now assumed to his worried mind the proportions of a nightmare.

"I suppose, sir," said the young lieutenant to whom he had first made himself known, "that you are here to tell us the garrison has already squashed those rioters."

Rioters!

Disgusted by such an airy understatement, Knight was relieved to find that the unit's C.O. was somewhat better informed as to the nature and intent of the men who now had Dublin in their grasp. But even he was inclined to take a poor view of their chances, and, above all, their capacity for endurance.

"This affair will blow itself out," he said with brisk assurance. "Those fellows will never be able to face a show-down—*if* it comes."

"*If* it comes?"

Knight's misery increased when he learned that the battalion was not to press on towards the city proper but stay halted for further orders. "It's said that the frocks are playing politics again," the C.O. said. "But you mustn't blame me for that . . ."

The hours went by. The sun began to wane. A shift of the breeze from the sea carried with it the mutter of distant rifles. For the first time the soldiers began to show signs of impatience.

*   *   *

While Knight was fretting and fuming about the lack of "resolute action", and threading his way through the area dominated by Daly's group, two other English visitors were regarding the Rising as a sort of holiday bonus.

One of these was a young actress—Kitty Francis—who had

47

arrived at the exclusive Shelbourne Hotel, overlooking St Stephen's Green just before noon, and had almost immediately been treated to the extraordinary spectacle of fellow guests —army officers—running to the hotel windows, revolvers in hand, to swap pot-shots with a group of young men on the pavement. No one was hurt. The firing died down. Miss Francis had a most delightful lunch.

She was not alarmed by the manager's tactful statement that "rebels" had taken over the Green. The Shelbourne—the opulent Shelbourne—seemed so deliciously *safe*. Her main sensation was one of joyous curiosity. This . . . this affair . . . was all so very, very Irish. It would give her something to write home about.

To Master Maclear Bate, aged eight, the morning had begun as happily as most mornings did when, on holiday from the detested boarding school near Worthing, he stayed with his grandfather in Kingstown's fashionable Eden Park. To young Harry such stays were periods of pure bliss . . . daily visits to the seashore . . . or cheerful journeys into the mountains . . . mounted on a cushion strapped to the crossbar of Grandpa's bike, he was also a frequent visitor to the city, where Mr Reginald Bate was held in respect by all, and considerable awe by some.

It looked at first sight an unlikely combination—a close comradeship between a mischievous small boy and a man who was noted for his dignity, and the conservatism of his ways. And yet, improbable or not, it really worked.

With Harry's father, his eldest son, a world away—on the China Station—and his younger sons serving their King and Country in the West, life was lonely for the austere official. Holy Tartar though some might well consider him to be— with his sternly waxed moustache and firm style of delivery —the old man showed a vastly different side to Harry. Life with Grandpa—recalls Mr Harold Bate—was, by contrast with school, sheer paradise!

It was on the afternoon of Monday the 24th of April that news came to Kingstown of "disturbances" in Dublin. As friends at the Yacht Club gathered around his Grandfather, young Harry could see the latter's face flush angry red. "Damn Sinn Feiners!" suddenly came from Mr Reginald Bate's taut lips. "I'd hang the lot of them!"

"I can't recall the rest of it," says Mr Harry Bate today. "But Grandpa had every right to be annoyed. You see, he was Solicitor to the Post Office—and the rebels had pinched his office!"

The holiday period was going to be more exciting than ever . . .

*   *   *

To Mrs Sarah Spellman—laying out her best silver in the drawing room of the trim little terrace house in North Side, Dublin—the first intimation of anything untoward occurring came with the news that the trams had stopped. Already wondering why her friends from the country should have been delayed, Mrs Spellman was considerably upset, and indignantly inveighed against "those Labour fellows", ready to ruin the holidays of the populace for the sake of a bob or two more. When she heard that the situation was something worse than that—and that the Sinn Fein traitors were actually shooting people her anger and contempt reached boiling point. A widow, she had no children of her own, but her late husband had always been a sturdy and uncompromising Unionist, and to Mrs Spellman his beliefs were sacrosanct. She had nephews risking their lives daily against the Kaiser's U-boats, yet these fellows were allowed to stay at home and feed on the fat of the land. Then, from south of the river came the pop-pop of machine guns.

Mrs Spellman rose from her table, and, with an air of great determination, put on the kettle. When the soldiers came to put this nonsense down they would surely be glad of a sip of tea. She also went to the medicine chest, and brought out a roll of bandages. In times like the present, you never knew. . . .

CHAPTER FOUR

For Kitty Francis, the "fun" of the rebellion—"bit of a lark" she had thought it, as she unpacked in her hotel room—came to an end that afternoon with merciless abruptness.

After lunch, disregarding the prospects of yet another revolver duel between the insurgents and her fellow guests, the officers, she had dared to venture into the sunshine, and idly watch the strange young men who had occupied St Stephen's Green start to dig a trench across the smooth green turf and erect a makeshift barricade outside the Shelbourne itself. The atmosphere was incongruously peaceful.

The volunteers worked leisurely, as though with plenty of time to spare. The aprons of the republican nurses, starched white as snow, shone brightly as those of children's nannies as they gossiped on the park benches. It was pleasantly warm. The budding elms scarcely moved in the windless air. Even the dry rattle of musketry—coming intermittently from the direction of the river—failed to excite or alarm. It seemed distant enough to be comfortingly impersonal. This was surely, Miss Francis reflected, the oddest of all rebellions. Or, come to think of it, the most Irish of all Irish stories. They'd kill themselves laughing, when they heard of it back home.

It was when a car approached from a side-street that Kitty Francis's peace of mind received its first upset.

"Halt," shouted a sentry.

The driver failed to react with sufficient speed, and the shout was followed by the whine of a bullet. Meant to warn, it missed the car, but hit an unfortunate onlooker standing by the Shelbourne's door. A moment later the young actress —still numbed by shock—became aware of an argument at the barricade.

The rebels had requisitioned a handcart to give strength to the structure's centre, and an old man—the cart's owner —had been lodging abusive protest. Now, maddened with anger, he started to pull at the cart to free it. Tragedy swiftly followed.

An officer tried to restrain him: the old man shook him loose. The officer tried again: the old man hit him. And then ... the incredible ... Somebody opened fire!

50

The old man jack-knifed, and collapsed across the pavement. Blood jumped from his chest, and spilled into the gutter. As the armed youths gawked in speechless and hopeless dismay, convulsions wracked him. He kicked out his feet and —quite suddenly—was dead.

It was at this point that Miss Francis decided to scream.

* * *

Less than half a mile to the north of St Stephen's Green and the Shelbourne, the great doors of Trinity College were slammed shut, and securely bolted. Some youths appeared on the roof, and were seen to be carrying rifles. Dressed in civilian clothes, they were at first mistaken for insurgents. That mistake was to cost the rebels very dear.

Trinity's impressive record as a centre of learning had earned it through the centuries the respect and admiration of scholars all over Europe. But the place had another distinction that was far less widely appreciated: it had become reserved almost exclusively for the sons of the Protestant Ascendancy. Generations of great soldiers, administrators and men of medicine had been nurtured behind its graceful time-mellowed walls—to serve the Empire with distinction in practically every clime. Geographically the College lay close to Dublin's heart, but the interests of its students were focused on broader horizons. Trinity's influence advanced with the spread of the red on the map.

That this fortress of the Establishment would have scant sympathy for "rebellion" was so obvious to the rebellion's leaders as to be almost axiomatic. What they did not appreciate was the need to guard against the effects of its active antagonism. In the context of a battle for the city, Trinity was no mere architectural ornament. Its position endowed it with a vital tactical importance.

Lying astride the southern approach to the O'Connell Bridge it dominated the direct road link between the rebel headquarters and their forces around the Castle. If held by forces hostile to the insurrection, it could sever that link, and, in addition allow direct fire to bear upon O'Connell Street itself. More, while the insurgents were bitterly regretting their dearth of arms, Trinity possessed a first-class arsenal: rifles by the score for its very keen O.T.C.

Such factors—it might have been thought—were formidable enough to have warranted the serious attention of those who planned to destroy, by force of arms, the very fabric of the political structure that the College held so dear. Oddly enough, it was not so. This rallying ground and sally-point for the loyalist reaction was ignored completely in the planning that preceded the rising, and did not feature in the list of objectives that the rebels aimed to occupy. It was tacitly assumed that Trinity—*should* the place be required—could be taken over as speedily as any other civilian dwelling. That the place might offer resistance, let alone be a menace to the whole conduct of the rising, was not appreciated, until too late.

Like everywhere else in Dublin on that most confusing of afternoons, the area around Trinity was crowded with promenaders. Despite the echo of the shooting in the Portobello area, and the wild doings in O'Connell Street the city was still in a completely hazy state as to what was happening and why.

Outside the Bank of Ireland—its curved pillared portico thrusting towards the greensward that lapped against the greystone wall—a group of bystanders were engaged in vehement argument.

"I tell youse," said one, "it's all a massive cod. It's manoeuvres they're performing, only they're making them more realistic. The shots you heard over there were blanks."

"And I'm telling *you*," answered another angrily, "that those bloody blanks are *real*. Sure haven't I seen for myself the bloody things KILL people!"

Next second the discussion was brought to sudden stop, by the scream of a bullet ricochetting on a roof.

The group looked all around them, in complete astonishment. And then came a wink of fire from a window of the College; followed by yet another frightening whine.

"By God," said someone, "we'd better get out of here!"

The first shots fired from Trinity—aimed rather wildly at a volunteer patrol—aroused pleasurable excitement among the students responsible. Lead by their O.T.C. drill sergeant and a professorial part-time officer, they had reacted to news of the rising with that prompt combativeness that was later said to be lacking among those from whom it might have been expected. The students had drawn rifles from the O.T.C.'s armoury, and sent out a call to their fellows throughout their city to rally to them "and defend the college".

Only twelve in number, they then waited tensely for the rebel attack. It did not come. By three o'clock the little force had doubled. And still the volunteers remained content with swapping shots. By evening, the chance to subdue Trinity had gone for good. The students had been joined by professional fighters: Canadians, South Africans and Anzacs on furlough who—with no source available to tell them what to do—had used their own initiative and "marched towards the sound of the guns . . ."

*   *   *

"Hopelessly bungled" was Lieutenant Collins' assessment of the military direction of the Rising, but this, like other strictures from the future Big Fellow, was to be lost sight of in later years by those carried away by the beauty of the "Idea, the heroism with which it was served, and the monumental influence its *defeat* was to exert on shaping Ireland's history." Yet, when considered from the purely military aspect, Collins' criticism was undoubtedly justified.

The failure to seize Trinity, the reluctance to press home the attack upon the Castle, the casual manner in which the plans to wireless news of the rising, and thus enlist world sympathy had been arranged, and then left to collapse . . . these were but symptoms of a fundamental fault in the rebels' direction of the rising.

Largely drawn by that talented but unstable amateur, Plunkett, the original blueprint for revolt had provided for the construction of a complicated network of key-points, barricades and trenches reaching from Kingstown in the south, to the northern suburbs on the coast road to Ulster. It was, in many ways, a remarkably thorough document, but based of course on the assumption that these elaborate defences would have a minimum of 4,000 men to build and man them. After the Countermanding Order, which meant that this figure would not be realised, it was obvious that the blueprint had become a liability: but no alternative was provided, nor even mooted. Thus, on the first day, the volunteers had wasted effort on defences that needed three times their numbers to complete and four times their numbers to hold—defences that, in many cases, were later to serve as cover for the Crown Forces whose advance they had been designed to prevent. The defence plan was also responsible for a singular failure of aggressive rebel reaction to British outflanking moves. In several cases this was to be attributable to the fact that local leaders had failed to appreciate that "positions" they had originally been told would cover flanks and rear existed only on paper: all hope of manning them having passed away with the disappearance of three out of every four volunteers on the eve of mobilisation.

Again, the original dispositions of the insurgents had been

designed with the further aim of dividing and sub-dividing the troops of the city's garrison into "penny packets." By isolating each individual barracks—it was argued—they would be prevented from making a collective intervention to assist the forces fighting in Dublin. Attractive though this plan may have appeared in the context of its time—and the confident forecast of a 100 percent mobilisation—it was now evident that it might contain the seeds of the rebellion's destruction.

Ebulliently the leaders boasted of their success in containing a force that was nearly twice the size of their own. What they were forgetting was the fact that the quiescence of the troops was not so much enforced by rebel strength as by initial surprise and—owing to the almost Byzantine politics of the affair—the need to wait for orders.

Portobello Barracks . . . Richmond Barracks . . . the Castle . . . in each of these centres, and half a dozen like them, waited in state of siege the forces of the garrison. But say they should try to unite? Say that those khaki limbs should stretch towards each other, and feel the weakness of the barriers between them? Who then—should this happen— would be besieger and besieged? Who, then, would be "split up into penny packets?"

*　　*　　*

The afternoon dragged on, with only minimal distractions from the Crown Forces in the city. The party at the Four Courts drove off a small force of infantry. Kearney's comrades on the tall chimnneys of Jacob's sniped away an attempt to approach the Castle from the west. In St Stephen's Green the Citizen Army contingent built up their defences.

The leader there—Commandant Mallin—continued to construct a ring of barricades around the road entrances to the Green and, as an additional insurance, occupied the adjacent College of Surgeons and placed riflemen in some of the houses. Yet there was one omission in his scheme of all-round defence: he still did not take possession of the Shelbourne.

From one of Mallin's sturdy commonsense—a former N.C.O. in the Indian Army, he had brought refreshingly practical views to bear on the more highflown ambitions of his colleagues—this neglect was rather surprising. The hotel dominated the whole defence area, and, should the British manage to seize it, the rebel positions would soon become untenable. Yet, inexplicably, Mallin did not seem to grasp the latent threat of this tall building to his rear. Pre-occupied with blocking the normal routes into the Green, and thus stopping a frontal assault, he appears to have given no thought to the possibility of British infiltrators penetrating the Shelbourne from the back, and thus turning it into a fortress from which the republicans on the Green could be enfiladed and put to flight. For once, the equable Mallin was guilty of an error of judgment.

Error of judgment too was the reaction of Connolly towards the "siege" of the Castle. He appeared to be quite happy that this stronghold of the British administration had not been taken. It was "contained" by the insurgent riflemen he argued, and no more was needed than that. Yet, even as he spoke, the "beleagured" Castle's very solid apprehensions were being set to rest. A detachment of the Royal Irish Rifles and the Dublin Fusiliers—intelligently avoiding the temptations for pitched battle that had proved so irresistible, and so costly, to their comrades—had succeeded in outflanking the rebel force at Portobello. Now, marching at the double, it had managed to reach Ship Street Barracks.

As a relief force, the column was not large. It represented slightly less than the strength of a full company; but it would very quickly make its presence felt. Gone were the rebel hopes of quickly capturing Dublin Castle. Soon the men there under the command of Connolly (no relation to James Connolly) would not even "contain" the garrison. Once given a chance, the soldiers would shoot them down like snipe.

As yet, however, these events were unguessed at, and nobody at headquarters appreciated the extent of the tactical blunders that threatened their plans with disaster. After all, their opponents' mistakes had been considerable. In general, the first tentative interventions of the military had ended in bloody reverses.

* * *

Miss Spellman's prudent preparations to aid the wounded would have been welcomed by the men of the Royal Irish Regiment, sent from their barracks to give the civil authorities "support" in coping with whatever it was that had befell the city.

The men were issued with live ammunition, but ordered not to charge magazines. This was because of the confusion that surrounded the news of the rising. Some still thought that they had to deal with a mere riot. Others that their presence was needed to dissuade the "Shinners" from reckless action. Officers were anxious not to encourage the trigger-happy.

They were scared of embarrassing "accidents". Unfortunately for the Royals, the Volunteers were less inhibited.

Marching in fours, with their unloaded rifles at the slope, the soldiers came under heavy fire from a group of Kent's men, protecting the flank of the force that had occupied the South Dublin Union. There were several casualties and the Royals were forced to take refuge in nearby houses.

To the east, an even worse misfortune was suffered by another British force—a company of "The G.R.'s"—from the 1st Dublin Associated Volunteer Training Corps, formed largely of old reservists and rejects on health grounds from the regular army.

The men were on routine exercises near Kingstown when they heard of the "disturbance". Spiritedly they decided they must do something about it; and promptly set out to march upon the city. The G.R.s had only a hotchpotch of antique firearms, including single-shot Martini carbines. Even more important, they hadn't a bullet between them. But they felt that Beggar's Bush barracks, which they would pass on their way, would remedy such technical deficiencies. In the meanwhile there was no dampening their cheerful and aggressive spirits.

The old soldiers—many of them were grandfathers—were singing Tipperary when the mauser bullets fell on them like hail. By tragic coincidence they had marched unsuspectingly into the sights of George Reynolds and his men in Lower Mount Street, part of de Valera's defenceline against the expected arrival of the reinforcements from England.

When the rebels ceased firing the broad avenue was strewn with bodies, five dead and seven wounded.

* * *

The tall statue of Justice above the portico of Dublin Castle had a peculiarity often remarked upon by the plain facetious or the ill-disposed. Its face was turned towards the Establishment, while it presented to the city only its stony back. On Easter Monday the disadvantages of this introspective stance were becoming evident, even to those who had hitherto been its beneficiaries. More, those disadvantages appeared to be becoming contagious: living men struck frozen attitudes, and saw not what went on.

News of "trouble" in Dublin had come to Whitehall belatedly, and at first was received with no undue sense of shock. A certain amount of reaction had been expected over the arrest of Casement: but only because it would symbolise the death of any hope of insurrection. The Countermanding Order—with its cancellation of the sinister-sounding "manoeuvres"—had encouraged the complacency of the civil servants surrounding Birrell. Like Nathan in Ireland he had seen the Order as conclusive proof of the defeat of Sinn Fein's extremist wing. There might be a riot or two; but Dublin was used to riots. Only later did doubts begin to populate the corridors of power . . .

"Serious disturbances," the Irish authorities had said. But just *how* serious? They did not seem to know. Some telephone lines were still in working order; but the vast majority were not. To get the first official news across to Britain a young officer had had to travel from Dublin to Kingstown in disguise and have his C.O.'s dispatch relayed by the naval wireless station. Only slowly, very slowly, did the picture begin to build up. A policeman shot dead by men trying to raid the Castle . . . the Lancers in action in O'Connell Street . . . troops fired on when attempting to cross the Liffey . . . but the impact of even these reports was blunted by the apparent contradictions. It had been confirmed that the provinces were quiet. It had been confirmed that some of the top men in the Volunteers had turned non-active, if only for the present, and, far from participating in "disturbances" were spending the day at home. And then, of course, there were the logistical arguments that weighed against the rumours of revolt being accepted at face value: material odds were now weighted so heavily in favour of the authorities that a coup de main was surely out of the question. Casement— "the arch villain"—was safely under lock and key. The arms and ammunition destined for his confederates now rested scores of feet beneath the sea. It was with these factors to influence its thinking that London still pressed "how serious?" But the answers from the Irish side continued to be confused.

Bonar Law himself intervened, in a personal attempt to make sense of the situation. He found that, irritatingly, it made no sense at all. Finally, thoroughly discontented with the service provided by the official channels, he reverted to an approach that, in those days, was a miracle of unorthodoxy. To complete the unhappiness of the bureaucrats, he asked the press to help him—the press in the person of none other than Max Aitken.

Tim Healey was in Dublin at the time. Could Aitken manage to make contact, and ask for his eyewitness account? The future Lord Beaverbrook succeeded in doing just that.

The conversation was brief, and, on Healey's part, not always to the point. It went like this.

"Is there a rebellion?"

"There is," came Healey's reply.

"When did it break out?"

"When Strongbow invaded Ireland!"

"When will it end?"

"When Cromwell gets out of Hell!"

CHAPTER FIVE

"We've beaten them," boomed Connolly. "I tell you, we've beaten them!" He beamed delightedly at the volunteers, blocking the Post Office windows with filing cabinets and desks, and then repeated his confident refrain. "We've beaten them . . ."

The men believed him.

Stock-taking at the end of the day, the insurgent leaders had good cause for satisfaction. Whatever the reservations of the young Michael Collins. They had proclaimed the Republic, and formed its "Provisional Government". They had stood by their purity of principle: their pretensions as soldiers of Ireland had been asserted in arms. The volunteer rank-and-file were equally cock a hoop. So often derided as a rabble, playing glorified cowboys-and-indians, they had not only stood fast against the seasoned troops of the imperial army: they had inflicted losses and forced them to withdraw. The tricolour now flew in all quarters of the city, and the "Government" was now installed in its very heart.

In short then, it appeared that the insurgents had more than fulfilled the role assigned them by Pearse and the I.R.B. They had rolled the ball at least "half way up the hill", to inspire others to join them, or succeed them, and help roll it all the way. Yet would this latter development—raison d'être of the whole affair—quickly materialise? It was here that the leadership had cause for disquiet.

Grandiloquently, the rebel writ was claimed to extend through the length and breadth of Ireland. In practical terms it was limited to Dublin itself. And, even here, the power to enforce it was ludicrously weak: stretched no further than the reach of a bullet from each of the widely scattered strongpoints. Again, "proclaim" it as much as they liked, the validity of that writ was not only rejected by the Westminster Government, the Opposition and the Parliamentary party headed by Redmond, it was hotly disputed inside the republican movement itself. The flouting of the Counter-manding Order, and the suspension of MacNeill, had not only bewildered the bulk of the volunteers: it had rent the Sinn Fein leadership from top to bottom. But it was the lack of response among average Dubliners to the clarion call for arms that provided a danger signal to the thoughtful, even though its glow showed but faintly against a sky flushed by the day's achievements.

For if *they*—the citizens of the capital—were truly representative in their reactions to Pearse's idealistic "summons to the Flag" then what could be expected from more conservative country cousins? When word got round of the losses sustained by the G.R.'s the Dublin crowd had promised lynch law for the "murderers" responsible, and Pearse had been forced to order his followers in no circumstances to fire on unarmed men. Further afield, the course of the Rising had provoked units of the Nationalist Volunteers to act against their former comrades while—in remote Westminster—it was to throw into temporary alliance, born of indignation, Irishmen as rootedly opposed as Carson and John Redmond.

In other respects too, the insurrection's pattern had gone awry. The seizure of the G.P.O. was to have been followed by news of the rising being telegraphed to all quarters of Ireland. Pearse's proclamation of the Republic was to have been wirelessed to America and the world. Global sympathy was to have been enlisted before the British could raise a word of condemnation. None of these things had happened.

While the line from British Army H.Q. at Park Gate to the Curragh still remained intact, the telegraph system which was to have resolved the confusion over the Countermanding Order, rallied waverers to the flag, and mobilised international support, had come to a stop with the rebels' takeover. In their efforts to cut British military communications they had succeeded in sabotaging their own publicity.

This break in contact was to have momentous consequences. The Limerick and Clare contingent, disbanded under the Countermanding Order only forty-eight hours before, had consisted of nearly 1,500 men. Dispersed to their homes they remained in complete ignorance of the Order's dramatic reversal. A similar situation prevailed in rebel-minded Wicklow. First Larry Wolohan heard of the rising was on Tuesday night: the news was broken to him by a sergeant of the R.I.C.!

When word of the Dublin upheaval did begin to filter through to the provinces, it was too late for anything but isolated individual action. The police had acted with ruthless speed: local leaders were under lock and key. Again, the original plan had emphasised the need for an intensive operation against British communications in the country areas. Bridges were to have been destroyed and railway lines uprooted, road blocks established to hamper British troop movements. And the men of the R.I.C.—the eyes and ears of the administration—rendered powerless by being pinned down in their isolated barracks. In the event, however, these measures were taken only on a limited scale. Most provincials were unaware that the time had come to implement them.

Late afternoon Monday, these facts of life as regards what was happening—or, rather, what was *not* happening—outside the city, had not penetrated the grey walls of the Post Office. While the first of the relief columns had installed itself in the Castle, a cavalry detachment from the Curragh had actually entered Dublin by train. It had arrived at Kingsbridge Station without incident—much to its own surprise —and had found the track there undamaged and the platforms undefended. Soon after the troopers de-trained they came under rifle-fire, probably from a detachment of Kent's force in the South Dublin Union, but the effect was slight. The officer in command of the column decided to push his luck a little further.

Having left a holding force in the station, the cavalrymen marched eastward at the double, slipping through the rebel outposts with an ease that was later to call for bitter comment. The garrison at Guinness's, intended to bar just such a movement as this—along the south bank of the Liffey to Kent's rear—did not report the troopers' presence, let alone react against them. A few individual shots were fired, and that was all. Rather breathless, and still bemused by its good fortune, the Curragh detachment, after a circling movement through the side streets, found itself, just before nightfall, installed in Dublin Castle.

This audacious coup of the cavalry was to have a fateful effect upon the whole course of the rising. At the time, however, it appears to have made very little impact on the calculations of the rebel leaders, whose attention was divided between the celebration of their triumphs of the morning, and an embarrassment that had arisen on their own front doorstep. It had taken them completely by surprise—the threat of mob anarchy.

*   *   *

"Halt," yelled the young volunteer, as the ragged crowd that had emerged from the slums that lay northeast of the Pillar, came swaying like a crocodile in drink towards the half-completed barricade.

"You're to come no further," he expostulated, rather unsurely. In a sort of drunken good humour the crowd continued to press on.

One of the boy's companions, rifle at port, came running across the street in an attempt to intervene. "You heard the order—get home and stay out of trouble . . ."

A giant roadworker stepped forward. "So *that's* the way of it!" With a laugh, he grabbed the rifle, wrested it loose, and tossed it through the nearest shop window. The volunteers shrank back.

"Help yourselves, good people," the giant invited, gesturing expansively towards the shattered glass. "Help yourselves to anything you want. Silk . . . sables . . . liquor . . . the best of everything. It's all on the house today!" He was answered by a cheer, and the rush of a thousand feet.

Clery's, the big departmental store, was one of the mob's first targets. Literally, they took the place apart. Then other shops fell victim to their violence.

Hands joined together, as if in ring-a-roses, street urchins danced through broken doors and windows; emerged bedecked with bangles and fancy jewellery. Toothless shawlies fist-fought over a heap of precious furs and tore at each other's scant white hair, until their scalps were bleeding. An enterprising man—a rag and bone dealer it was said—pushed his way through the turmoil leading a donkey and cart, and loaded up with furniture and bedding.

"Help yourselves," the giant had roared. They helped themselves.

It had been with near-incredulity that the predatory poor had seen the police withdraw—under orders—from the streets. It was too good to be true: smacked too much of a trap. And next they had waited—and dreaded—the inevitable sequel, the avenging advent of the military. Yet all that had happened had been the futile charge of the lancers. And now the new masters—the victorious insurgents—had vanished from the scene. They were busy at work in the G.P.O. and the other buildings they had earmarked for their strongholds. Except for a few scattered pickets, there was no sign of the forces of Law.

" Good love us," an old lady was heard to remark. "'tis free for all now, *and* with the blessing of providence!"

The metallic crunch of sledgehammer and pick could be heard above the clamour of the mob, as the volunteers pushed loopholes through the brickwork, or pierced connecting walls to give them covered communications between buildings. And the voices of the volunteers could be heard as well, singing the songs traditional to the Irish in rebellion. But, though heard, the new authorities remained unseen. They had boasted of seizing the city, but exerted no direct sway. The most fashionable shops and dwellings were now temporarily unprotected, and the dispossessed battened on them, like hungry birds of prey.

In O'Connell Street, two prostitutes, drunk as their escorts, stripped down and changed threadbare shifts for evening gowns. Staid housewives looped the linen they had looted around their shoulders like white bandoliers. And from the pub a few doors from Clery's the giant and his cronies dispensed to all the inspiration of alcohol.

Where the tramlines, littered with torn-open hat boxes, marched down towards the Liffey . . . down in the blood-soaked dust that no corporation workman came to clear . . . a dead troop horse lay, stripped of its stirrups and saddle. A woman—consumptively coughing—swayed feebly over it, and patted it, and squatted comfortably on its rump. From the recesses of her patched flannel petticoat she pulled out a rosary, and a bottle of gin: and then, in broken tones, began to sing.

It was a song of sighing seas, and misty islands, of shadows riding on the green of western mountains . . . of an innocence lost, perhaps never to be regained.

* * *

"Whereas an attempt, instigated and designed by the foreign enemies of our King and Country to incite rebellion in Ireland and thus endanger the safety of the United Kingdom has been made by a feckless though small body of men who have been guilty of insurrectionary action in the city of Dublin, we Ivor Churchill do hereby warn . . ."

It was a tight-lipped and angry Lord Wimborne who prepared and signed the proclamation. Tight-lipped and angry he remained when it was issued. After a brief inspection of the troops who now ringed the Vice-regal Lodge he excused himself and retired into his study. There he grimly sat down and wrote a letter. It was addressed to Augustine Birrell.

"The worst has happened," he wrote, "just when we thought it had been averted. If only we had acted with decision last night it would have been averted . . ."

Even if ignored by the Chief Secretary, the implied reproach would not be lost on others . . .

* * *

Night came to Dublin, and, with the night, fresh trials. From that mixed bag, the garrison of Trinity, came intermittent flurries of rifle-fire, aimed by "Colonials" and students and the youths of the O.T.C., and professors who shut their eyes every time they pulled trigger. Planned to deter attackers from mustering in the shades beyond the Bank, these activities claimed few victims though among them were two harmless civilians. From the insurgent positions came a brisk return, equally futile and wasteful of precious bullets, and equally contributing to the respectable citizen's discomfort and alarm. Rumours of troop movements were circulating by the score. It was said the Castle had been further reinforced; a report subsequently confirmed by a crescendo of machine-gun fire, aimed at the insurgents in City Hall. It was said that the cavalry from the Curragh had been ambushed and destroyed: an example of wishful thinking at total variance with the facts. A German division had landed in the West . . . the West had risen as a man to march on Dublin . . . British warships in Dublin Bay were threatening bombardment . . . at least the rumourmongers had never had it so good.

In O'Connell Street, however, the rebel leadership was still largely preoccupied with the problem posed by the looters. Earlier it had been thought that the appetite of the mob had been sated. But now, after a brief dispersal, its separate components had started to form a whole again; its presence a challenge to the very name of the self-styled "Government". "Why not teach them a lesson?" a civic dignatory pleaded. The question was easy to put, but not so easy to answer.

The dilemma of the insurgent leaders was peculiar, and unenviable. Attempts at a solution were hampered by the desperate idealism of their image. The thought of applying the brutally simple methods of crowd disposal hallowed by tradition was unwelcome, to say the least. How could they be adopted by rebels against the very authority that those measures had upheld? Nor was it certain that the insurgents —understrength, and widely scattered as they were—would have the means to impose complete control; even should they decide to revert to the practices of the past. Yet it was plain that mere appeals would cut no ice. Connolly himself had intervened, to plead with the crowd in the late afternoon. And this—this fresh influx of half-demented, loot-hungry rabble—now showed how little even his great influence counted when weighed against the prospects of easy-gain. Despite this depressing reflection, however, the dilemma remained acute. To do *something* would mean a clash with the very people whose lot the rebellion's leaders sought to better. To do *nothing* would serve to alienate still further the broad-mass of the law-abiding. The leaders of the insurrection were still undecided when, as if to emphasise the emotional, as well as the tactical, complexities of the situation, the rioters burst into the song of the Fenians . . .

"God save Ireland sang the heroes,
God save Ireland sing we all,
Whether on the battlefield we die
Or upon the gallows high
God save Ireland everyone . . ."

It was perhaps not surprising that so emotive a refrain—sung though it was in drunken bathos—should have moved to sentiment some of the officers in the Post Office. Dreamers and poets, the Sinn Fein leaders tended to credit all Irishmen —once aroused—with the virtues of their volunteer followers. Nurtured on legend, absorbed in the service of the National Idea, they had little knowledge of the pressures and treacheries engendered by grinding poverty that could shape and mis-shape this collective noun, "the People", whose cause they so sincerely believed they represented. On the other hand, their temporary allies—the representatives of the socialist Citizen's Army—were even more allergic to the use of force against those whom they regarded as the victims of exploitation. The crowds were allowed to sing on—and the wanton disorder continued.

The scruples of the staff officers in headquarters were not always shared by the hard-pressed pickets on the streets. Anger was slowly mounting among the volunteers as the mob's unruliness grew wilder. In one young officer this sentiment mixed with disgust and fused suddenly into fury.

Not content with their spoils from the shops, a group of looters turned their attention to some of the chairs and tables he had been using to establish a road-block.

"Hands off!" he shouted. "You leave those damn things alone . . ."

"Hell with *that*," came the reply. The men grabbed at a chair and started to heave it loose from the ropes that bound it to the rest of the barricade.

The officer glanced at his detachment—half a dozen volunteers—and snapped the command "Fix bayonets!"

Alas, he had forgotten. They had no bayonets to fix!

His face flushed at the titter: then once more the mob

surged forward. The young officer's hand dropped to his shiny-new holster.

"Halt!" he said firmly. The muzzle of the Browning was jammed securely into the ringleader's stomach.

A brief silence fell, followed by howls of protest. But the drunk did nothing to goad on his sympathisers. Sweat poured down his face. His body twitched. His eyes rolled whitely as he stared at the black-blue steel.

"I'll count to five," said the officer, "then tell my men to open fire. And this fellow here will be the first to go!"

Surly mutterings, broken by a cry, "For God's sake, go away all of yez. Don't you see the man means what he says. . . ."

"I'll begin to count," said the officer. "One . . . two . . ."

There were cries of appeal, changing to shouts of fear. By the time the count had reached three the mob were already in flight.

The officer sighed, a long sigh of relief, and slid the automatic back into its holster. The volunteers sighed too, and ordered arms. The drunk collapsed on his knees, mouthing choked words of thanks.

"Get out of it," said the officer. "And never bloody well come back!"

The crisis was over; but not for long.

The mob had invaded a toy store and "captured" several score union jacks. These they now heaped in the middle of the street, and made a bonfire of them. The volunteers looked on tolerantly at this popular performance. Then, suddenly there was another blaze: the Cable Shoe shop had been set alight.

Reluctantly the rebel leadership—all appeals to reason failing—issued the order that it hated so much to give. "Fire over the heads of the crowd. . . ."

*   *   *

For Captain Elliotson, squatting in the dusk on a rooftop of Dublin Castle, there were none of the inhibitions that affected Connolly, urging his men repeatedly "fire only to frighten, do not fire to kill." But Elliotson had no mere rioters to cope with, but armed rebels fairly strongly positioned, and desperadoes, as he put it, to a man. A professional soldier with an extremely lively intelligence, the Captain had been with the first column of Curragh troops to reach the Castle. He was in command of a machine-gun section, and eager to set it to work.

The City Hall . . . the offices of the Express and Star . . .
an outfitter's shop in Cork Street . . . these were the main
positions from which the rebels, to quote Connolly,
"dominated and besieged" the massive architectural symbol
of the British administration. Since their former leader's
death their major detachment, in the City Hall, had been
commanded by a tough Volunteer officer, a Dubliner in his
'twenties called James Reilly, and had intensified, if anything,
their vigorous campaign of sniping, and, though it had been
evident for hours that the Castle was no longer in danger of
direct assault, their fire was costing repeated casualties.

Among the officers in the garrison patience was wearing
thin. They were eager for attack. They were convinced that a
determined offensive would completely rout the unseasoned
rebels. Now, as evening fell, there were signs that their
ambitions were to be very shortly gratified.

Off-duty nurses were roused from their brief rest, and sent
into the wards to warn the wounded to be ready for the noise
of the machine-guns. Fresh bandages were prepared. All
instruments sterilised. All blinds were pulled down, and all
the lights turned out.

The Crown Forces were at last to attempt the clearance
of the Castle's besiegers, and their first objective was the City
Hall. Elliotson's gunners were to give them covering fire.

The troops attacked at the sound of a whistle. They went in
at a dash, with rifle and bayonet. And then they came
staggering back, with heavy loss . . .

Furiously Elliotson ordered his men to fire in long bursts
—sending bullets by the hundred every minute into the
Georgian brickwork of the strongpoint, seeking out and find-
ing their way through every opening in the barricaded
windows. Steam rose from the Vickers guns in clouds. Dust
from shattered ceilings and walls fogged the rebel defenders,
their eyes streaming and choking while bullets ricochetted
wildly, claiming victims. But still they stood firm.

Connolly sent reinforcements from O'Connell Street at the
double. They arrived in time to stop yet another determined
onslaught. Rebel morale rose to cheering point—even among
the women's detachment sent for safety to the cellar—while
Elliotson and his brother officers were forced to reconsider
their tactics. The machine-guns ceased to fire. There fell an
uneasy silence.

At one point the City Hall was separated by only a few
yards from the walls of the Castle. But to reach it the soldiers
would have had to emerge from a side-gate and double

back, thus exposing themselves to the fire of Reilly's marksmen on the roof. Now as the assault parties licked their wounds and counted their dead the surviving officers came to an imaginative decision. It was death, they decided, for their men to attack across the bullet-swept pavements: instead, *they would move underneath them.*

Someone had discovered that the vast cellars of the Castle stretched beyond the limits of its walls; in fact they reached to below the City Hall, and troops proceeding through them could reach a point where access to the street could be obtained through a manhole almost below the enemy's front doorstep.

To react against such a force—emerging in "dead ground" —Reilly's men would have to break cover. It was Elliotson's job to see that they did not, or that, if they did, they would not succeed in regaining it. Once more in the Castle Yard a whistle blew . . . the attack was on.

The Vickers burst into fresh fury, and desperately the rebels answered back.

"Why the hell don't they send their infantry against us?" a volunteer yelled to Reilly. They did not notice—until too late—the men in khaki swarm upward through the very surface of the street.

Reilly grabbed his rifle, and gallantly jumped to his feet, to brave the bullets and bring fire to bear on the attackers. But Elliotson's machine-guns brought down a barrage of lead and with a shout to his men, the rebel leader fell dead. Below, hurling hand-grenades at doors and windows, the cheering troops swept on.

It was bloody work in the Hall. A battle fought in a darkness lit only by the flash of rifle and pistol and the yellow-red explosions of the bombs. The ferocity of the fire that was aimed at them from landings and side doors twice forced the Tommies back, but then, with great courage, they re-formed and charged again.

Briefly they were held by the barricade on the staircase. Two minutes later the savage fight was over.

Shivering with shock, coughing from the bitter dust, their noses twitching to the stench of cordite, their ears still deafened by the uproar that had raged above them, the women who had accompanied the insurgents emerged from the cellar, and stumbled their way through the debris and the dead to be herded at bayonet point by angry and blooded soldiers, restrained only by their officers from outrage. Only a handful of rebels now remained at liberty: men who had sought a dubious refuge with the marksmen on the roof.

* * *

While the City Hall went through its agony, and the volunteers north of the river were coping with their country-men turned rioters, their comrades on the south side were still receiving the rude attentions of those who had declared themselves for the Crown.

At one of the rebel posts in the southern suburbs there were fears that local residents, might attempt a counter-stroke. The district was well-to-do, and populated by a class to whom the ownership of sporting guns and revolvers came as "natural" as golf clubs and tennis racquets.

On Monday night there were reports of male residents meetings in groups and passing resolutions of loyalty to King and Country which were accompanied by pledges to put down the "traitors". By the morning, however, it became plain that these sentiments were not going to be carried to extremes. The residents were not wanting in personal courage, but certainly they were wanting in organisation and direction. Ex-colonels and majors and captains of fighting Irish regiments . . . irate though their eloquence might be it prevailed but little against the instinctive aversion of their neighbours to anything that was not ordered, or at least approved, by the hallowed "established channels." And resistance on the part of awed amateurs, it was now said, was something that those channels would frown upon; fighting must be left to the regular forces.

Wimborne's proclamation had now begun to go the rounds. The rebels used copies of it for highly personal purposes, and the loyalists hotly argued about the implications of one of its phrases. The Viceroy had appealed "to all loyal and law-abiding citizens" to abstain from acts or conduct "which might interfere with the action of the Executive Government." This, said those in favour of inaction, meant that freelance intervention would only add to the confusion and embarrass the authorities: and, though much disputed, their opinion carried the day.

In the working-class districts, however, the appeal—or rather their interpretation of its meaning—fell on less responsive ears: if indeed it had been heard at all.

* * *

For the shelter that Jacob's provided from the insults of the women, Kearney and his friends were duly grateful.

Certainly the place had not many other claims on their gratitude.

Stumbling over machinery, sacks of grain and packing cases, they had been led to their positions through a blackness that had cost them torn shins and loss of temper. "We are surely the most irritated body of men that ever went out to fight for freedom in any country or clime," the poet recorded with sick humour. Many would have agreed.

Eventually Kearney's section was positioned by a grey blur that turned out to be a window, told to smash the glass and fortify it, and "hold to the last." They overlooked they knew not what, and didn't really care. Nor, during the long night, did anyone bother to remedy their ignorance or comfort their general sense of frustration and neglect.

Only when daylight came—after a series of false alarms that prevented them from sleeping—did the tired men realise that their rifles were trained on the houses of Bishop Street, just fifteen yards away. Had Kearney at any time turned jumpy, and pulled trigger, he would very likely have shot a peaceful citizen, in bed in the parlour opposite.

After the man had been awoken from the slumber that could so easily have proved fatal and had been evacuated to a neighbour's house—to the accompaniment, one suspects, of quite unprintable protests—Kearney's party set about strengthening their position. It was hours later, when they learned, in an exhausted lull, that their effort had been wasted. They should have been installed in a window to the *rear* of the building, looking out on the tall tenements of Bride Street —a likely objective for troops in search of cover.

"When," asked a volunteer hopefully, "will the men from the country reach us?"

His officer merely shrugged, and turned away.

Throughout Monday afternoon and early evening the soldiers whom Mrs Spellman had so confidently predicted would arrive at any moment—"and teach those corner boys manners"—had failed singularly to put in an appearance. Instead by the time darkness fell she had heard such alarming tales of rebel successes—not to mention rumours of "atrocities"—that even her curiosity as regards what had been happening refused to accept such evidence. She had slammed the door, and refused to listen any longer.

Now, when she opened it again, it was in response to a plea so unexpected that she could hardly credit it.

The voice through the letter-box was that of a jarvie who had known her late husband. "I've got two soldiers with me,

70

Mrs Spellman. For God's sake, ma'am, will yez take them off me hands?"

What a very odd request!

"Sure, I can't hide them," the jarvie persisted. "The childer would have it out in next to no time. But we can't let these fellows get shot."

"You mean," she said, astounded, "that someone is out to kill them? . . ."

"The rebels, ma'am!"

She threw open the door.

Mrs Spellman's first impression of the two fugitives was how very young they were. Boys in their late teens. The oddity of the fact that one of them was wearing a civilian raincoat, and the other the jarvie's slightly mildewed greatcoat over their uniforms, and that they now produced their peaked stiff caps from concealment beneath their armpits, registered only as secondary to her surprise at their youth. As soldiers, they looked so very unimpressive."

"Don't stand there all day," she said. "Come inside and sit you down."

One of the pair was Irish, from the West. The other had the distinctive twang of the cockney. They told her they had chummed up together when on leave, and had been near St Stephen's Green when the shooting had begun. A friendly publican had lent the raincoat, then handed them over to the jarvie who had done the rest. There were rebels everywhere, they'd been told. It was impossible to get to the Castle. The bridge across the canal to Portobello Barracks was held by the damned Sinn Feiners. A policeman had been shot dead when bravely refusing to hand over the key to St Stephen's Park. Another policeman had been killed when attempting to halt the rebels attacking Dublin Castle.

Mrs Spellman sighed. "I'll get you some supper," she said. "And you can stay in the spare room, if you like, until things blow over."

If the rebels get to know, she thought uneasily, we'll probably all of us be murdered in our beds.

But never let it be said that an Irishwoman would allow fear to stop her doing her duty.

* * *

"I really don't know," Lord Wimborne was to declare huffily, when asked who had given the C-in-C permission to go on leave on the very eve of the rising. "It's part of the system in Ireland," he added, with a sort of despairing

71

impotence. "Everyone seems to go away independent of everyone else. There is no co-ordination."

On Monday night, the man who was to be the scapegoat for the "system" that had given His Excellency, and others before him, such good cause for bemused frustration, was gently relaxing in London, quite oblivious to the commotion that had broken out behind his back, or the blame-shifting that was to damage his conscientious, though not unduly spectacular, career.

Friend's appointment as G.O.C. Ireland had been coupled with that of I/C Administration, Irish Command. In this duality of roles was reflected both the War Office's attitude towards Ireland—as a sort of glorified Aldershot—and its appreciation of his virtues as an administrator.

At 58, Friend had no experience of commanding forces in the field. Commissioned into the Royal Engineers at the age of seventeen, he had at one time been in charge of the Coast Defences of Scotland. Posted to Egypt, he was appointed, in his forties, Director of Works and Director of Warlike Stores. He had been given the Irish Command as recently as 1914, when it was felt that war on the continent would call for younger men; or men with more of an "acceptable" background. Military snobbishness still had a strong hold upon the Horse Guards, despite sporadic efforts at reform. For command in the field, a cavalryman was usually first choice: in some minds a commission's importance was related to the financial cost involved, in "living up to it," and R.E. messes were more frugal than most. But there were positive reasons too for posting Friend to Ireland. As a training ground and garrison area—with its own "frocks" to swell the multitude of "frocks" who now so irritatingly interfered with the day-to-day affairs of the army in England and Scotland, Ireland exacted a vast amount of paperwork from its military authorities, and Friend, it was admitted, knew how to handle such stuff. Again, Irish "frocks" were more volatile and sensitive than most: Friend's experience with Egyptians should stand him in good stead. "A quiet backwater" ran an appreciation of Ireland's role in wartime. It was to be cruel luck for the G.O.C. that this assessment was to prove false: an even crueller stroke was to be his absence from his station.

On Monday night Friend felt in the best possible of moods. With a prescience that, perhaps, would have surprised even his very best friends, he had been willing and anxious, weeks before, to have staked his career on arresting "those fellows"

72

in Ireland who, he was still confident, had been up to no good, but the authorities had been quick to overrule him, and maybe he had since reflected, they had been very right to do so. By all accounts, tension had eased since then, and Casement's arrest should put the kibosh on all that remained of the malcontents' hopes and schemes.

London, even in wartime, looked pretty good to Friend. Next morning, he decided, he would take a walk in the park. He loved Spring flowers—had been nostalgic for them in Egypt—and the daffodils and tulips would be a treat to see. He would take the dog for a walk through St James's, and then, perhaps, call at the Horse Guards. Purely as a matter of courtesy, of course.

* * *

At 3.30 on Tuesday morning thoughts of spring flowers were far removed from the mind of Brigadier General W. H. M. Lowe, commander of the reserve cavalry in the Curragh and now taking operational control of all the Crown Forces in Dublin. Crop in hand, he paced the platform of Kingsbridge station, while his men—whose steeds had been sensibly left behind—tumbled from the train and clumsily assembled, with much clattering of boots and rifle butts, in the darkness of the yard. It was icy cold, and, as he paced, the engine behind him hissed and blew off sparks as if deliberately to give snipers a point of aim, while sergeants cursed the ranks for rousing the neighbourhood. An odd sort of place for a frontline, Lowe was heard to remark to an aide. This fact, however, did not unduly worry him.

Owing to the critical failure of the rebels to destroy the Park Gate telephone network, word of the rising had come to this tall and slightly stooping professional cavalryman within forty minutes of its outbreak, and, though this was not appreciated at the time by a city expecting immediate spectacular action, he had acted with speed and decision.

It was Lowe who had sent an advance force—the one containing the redoubtable Captain Elliotson—to test the practicability of reinforcing Dublin by rail, and establish if possible a route of advance towards the Castle. And it was Lowe who had then alerted the cavalry's mobile column in the Curragh, and spread the warning to the army's provincial commands. But he had abstained from the temptation of immediate big-scale action; or an immediate personal appearance in the capital. First there were jobs of administration to be done: and Lowe knew precisely what.

The Assistant Adjutant General—Colonel H. V. Cowan —had asked urgently for a march on Dublin. Coolly, Lowe had decided he must wait. His attack would be no improvised affair, going off at half-cock, but one that would settle the rebels once for all.

A call had gone out for England to send troops: they would land at Kingstown, to the south, and North Wall, to the east. The support of troops from Ulster had been invoked: already a column was on its way from the north. The 24th Irish infantry brigade—Lowe's own command— would move upon the city from the west. Completely in the dark as to the strength of the insurgents, the Brigadier was determined to take no chances.

Now, with his arrival at Kingsbridge, Lowe felt that the strategical planning stage of the campaign had been satis- factorily concluded, and that he could at last assume direct tactical control.

As he saw it, he must concentrate on aims that—while making only economical demands on his available manpower —would pave the way towards the "quartering" of the rebel positions in the city once the promised massive reinforcements had arrived from England and the north. He must first, by establishing strongpoints and "masking" the South Dublin Union, make secure the "corridor" to the Castle. And then, to the Castle's east, control the multiple road complex represented by Stephen's Green. By this means, the rebels south of the river would be divided by a line drawn West to East. A vertical division—South to North—would come later, with the English attack from Kingstown . . .

CHAPTER SIX

Monday night brought Kitty Francis a heart-beating sense of dread, and the sour taste of a hangover she had done nothing at all to earn. Awakening from too-short and fretful sleep, she lay for a full minute puzzling about her fright. Just why was she fully clothed? And lying on top of the coverlet instead of being beneath it? And then, very starkly, she remembered.

The bystander shot down outside the Shelbourne's door ... the old man crumpling dead beside the barricade ... her screaming flight to the security of the foyer ... the memories came back in a heap. She began to shiver.

It was much later when she dragged herself to her feet. Somehow she *must* look out at the world beyond this prison of a room. Despite the warnings of the management to keep away from the windows—warnings emphasised at one stage by a stream of rebel bullets—she simply *must* see what was happening. Hugging the wall with her body, Miss Francis took a cautious peek from the very edge of the heavy hanging curtains, dodged back, and peeked again.

The night sky was serene. Stars loitered in and out of a whispy white fleece of cloud. The city streets seemed extra dark and, unaware of de Valera's action at the gasworks, she wondered why. Also she returned to wondering at the silence. The sound of firing from the direction of the Castle had been so intense before she dropped to sleep that she had covered her ears with her hands, and felt the veins throb as fiercely as if their motions were designed to tear at her brain.

Beneath the window, a man emerged briefly from the shadows. Slouch-hatted, slightly humped beneath the long rifle that sloped high above his left shoulder, he advanced a few paces, then disappeared again. His cough sounded loud in the stillness. Miss Francis glanced once more towards the Green, and, as she did so, felt a sudden stirring of sentiment, a twinge almost of pity.

The rebels were no longer the frightening monsters of yesterday afternoon, but merely weary men and women seeking rest. They lay huddled on the park benches, or beside the flower beds beneath the slight-stirring elms. Some had blankets over them. Others had covered themselves with news-

papers, that rustled in the rising pre-dawn breeze. There was
an air of helplessness, almost of pathos, about those dark
shapes, and Miss Francis, in that moment of mixed emotions,
suddenly wondered what would become of them all. Then
fear and anger at her own plight again took control of her
feelings. She could hear stealthy movements in the corridor,
and the whispering of men. The rebels, at long last, must be
taking over the hotel.

"For God's sake be careful with that bloody thing!"

The whispers were broken by a sudden bump, and followed
by a string of outraged blasphemy.

"Silence, you men!"

A voice that had the snap of anger in it. A voice that was
authoritative, upper-U and *English*.

Miss Francis ran to the door.

* * *

Seven British soldiers were moving along the corridor. An
officer and six men. They were carrying between them two
cumbersome burdens—the barrel and tripod of a Vickers'
machine-gun.

"Tommies!" panted Miss Francis, in an intonation of
ecstasy.

Scores of doors opened, as other guests came out to greet
the soldiers. There was even the start of a cheer, which the
officer promptly silenced. "As from now, this hotel is in the
frontline . . ."

Sobered, the guests allowed themselves to be marshalled
together and led to a safer part of the building. Soon the
Shelbourne's long mirrors threw back the reflections of sandbags, ammunition boxes and gleaming bayonets.

A maidservant ran up to the officer. Her face was streaming
with tears. "Glory be to God for the like of you, sir. Will
yez chase the rebels away now?"

The officer smiled.

Under Elliotson's command, he and his men had managed
to reach the hotel through the same combination of outrageous audacity and good luck that had enabled them to
relieve the Castle. It had happened like this:

After clearing the rebels from the City Hall, they had
commendably been prepared to sortie in search of further
success: but were uncertain as to what to aim at. When they
heard that Mallin had not occupied the Shelbourne the news
seemed too good to be true.

To the military mind it was obvious that the hotel held

the key to the St Stephen's Green position—in fact *so* obvious that the officers feared a trap. But say that it wasn't? The risk was great, but greater still was the prize. For, if the Shelbourne provided the key to St Stephen's Green, the Green itself could be said to act in the nature of a door. Slam it shut, and you'd cut the line of communication between the rebels' H.Q. and their outposts to the south. Throw it open, and the British reinforcements, hourly expected, could move against the insurgents besieging Trinity. And, after that? The way would lie open to O'Connell Bridge, and a direct assault on the insurrection's heart!

Scouts of Elliotson's force began to infiltrate the narrow streets around the Castle within minutes of receiving their orders. Now the rebels on the Green lay helplessly in their gun sights.

"When do we open fire, sir?"

"We'll wait until first light. Then give 'em all we've got . . ."

* * *

The sky paled over Dublin. Soon the mountains would show their heads in a purple blur. Over the sealine, miles beyond the Bay, the dark waters turned to silver.

In O'Connell Street, a volunteer sentry shuddered and cursed for the umpteenth time the fact that he had been too proud to clothe himself against the cold. He had not been able to afford to buy a military coat, and a civilian one, he had felt, would have spoilt the glamour of his tunic. Furtively he broke off his measured patrol, to fumble in the still smouldering debris of the Shoe Company's gutted shop, and feel the hot bricks with his hands. "Never mind, Michael," said his mate, with inapt cheerfulness. "By the look of the sky it will be a lovely day . . ."

His ear cocked to the sound of a machine-gun, tapping away south of the river. "What the hell's going on over there? Is it a battle they're after fighting?"

"Letting off steam, maybe, to keep themselves from freezing."

* * *

A few minutes earlier, in St Stephen's Green, the Citizen Army was beginning to stir from sleep. Two young men had begun to deepen a trench while one of their comrades—still yawning—sat up and watched. Two others lay a few yards away, asleep on the top of a car.

Elliotson took a look at the scene, and decided to wait no

77

longer. While his men had been so cautiously installing themselves in the hotel two of the damn rebels had been asleep on the walk outside. Too close for comfort. Far too close.

Crisply he ordered "Open Fire!"

The machine-gun burst into demoniac song. The young men fell backwards, legs in air, as if hit by a hose. Their comrade jumped from the car, and reached the cover of the elms. Two more died where they lay, and the machine-gun shifted its fire.

Wickedly it traversed the Green from left to right, and back again. It drew smouldering lines across the velvet-smooth turf, and hurled it upward . . . a myriad little globules of green that danced and twisted as if each were endowed with a separate, and tormented, life of their very own. Its bullets caught a rebel on the run . . . lifted him from his feet and hurled him upwards, then hit him again before his body flopped to earth: and next, the men and women on the benches were caught in the beaten zone of screaming lead.

When daylight came St Stephen's Green was clear—clear except for the litter of dead and wounded—and a diehard element in the furthest side of the Park. The bulk of the rebels had been forced to withdraw to the nearby College of Surgeons. There they were to remain—unable to play any further effective part in the rising—for four agonising days.

* * *

"Our fellows have got a mauling on the Green," the whisper went round. It was dismissed immediately as "an enemy lie."

As Commandant-General, Pearse had issued a proclamation about the progress of the rising, a good five hours after the machine-guns had opened fire. Yet he gave no hint of anything but success.

"The G.P.O. was seized at 12 noon," this remarkable document recorded, "and the Castle was attacked at the same time." No mention was made of the attack's repulse.

"Irish troops hold the City Hall," the proclamation continued: yet the bulk of the building had been seized by the cavalry a good eight hours before. And the last remnants of the rebel forces there—the men on the roof—had been forced to surrender at dawn.

"British attacks have everywhere been repulsed," was another line hard to vindicate from an author enjoying such a high reputation for personal integrity as Padraic Pearse. Was he *really* so ignorant of the St Stephen's Green debacle?

Or was the proclamation a mere propaganda instrument designed to impress friends abroad, and keep morale from sagging among the headquarters' garrison?

If considered in this latter light, the proclamation may be said to have fulfilled its objective. But it did little to simplify the very grave practical difficulties with which the insurgent posts elsewhere were soon to find themselves confronted, and its note of success lulled into complacency more than one garrison in the southwestern sector, when the British troops commenced to outflank them.

Apparently happy in the belief that their comrades were still firmly established on their left, they repeated the same error that they had made the day before—when Elliotson's detachment had been allowed to infiltrate through to the Castle. They stayed where they were—and did precisely nothing.

*　*　*

Though dedicated enough to be risking his life for "Free Ireland", Collins had felt from the start that the rising was doomed to disaster. Too many people were giving orders.

The young Volunteer lieutenant respected the idealism of Pearse, but the poet's ebullience on the course of the fighting appears from all accounts to have left him pretty well cold. Nor did Collins derive much comfort from his studies of the other two leaders of the "military" side of the movement. Plunkett—whose aide he was—was now so sick that he could hardly stand, let alone make decisive decisions: his brilliant mind had been reduced to a state of bewildered impotence spurred and be-salved, he was prey to exhibitionism. Conversely Connolly—worshipped though he was by the rank-and-file—was the victim, largely, of his own iron will. The very strength of it, made him a tremendous natural leader; it was the route along which he led that was uncertain. Defiant of difficulties, when principles were concerned, he expected lesser men to measure up to his own stature—and pitted them against the most outrageous odds. To Collins, the whole structure of the rebel command seemed wasteful and top-heavy. There were too many officers, and far too few men. On Monday, when others were blind to all but the insurrection's initial triumph, he had sourly described the atmosphere as that "of a Greek tragedy."

By Tuesday morning the strength of the Big Fellow's analogy was being supported by some pretty significant facts. The volunteers on the barricades had been told that help would come from the provinces: disconcertingly, the provinces stayed quiet. They had been told—and the leadership believed—that the hundreds of volunteers who had left the city for the holiday while ignorant of the decision to reverse MacNeill's directive would swell their ranks as soon as they returned. This had not happened.

Incredibly, by noon Tuesday, the total insurgent strength stood at only a few more than that of the day before.

Loyalty to MacNeill? Indignation at the usurpation of his authority? Fright at realising that, once committed to rebellion, there could be no turning back? The reasons for neutrality varied from man to man, as such reasons usually do: but looming large among them appears to have been the hostility of public reaction.

Held up at checkpoints, forced to make long detours to their homes, informed that the trams weren't running, and the gas was "off", the crowds that streamed back to Dublin on Monday night had developed an ugly mood. They were sick with anxiety for their families and friends. They feared the inevitable reaction of the Crown forces. The name Sinn Fein was something at which to spit. "Bits of boys in fancy uniforms" . . . "corner boys and counter-jumpers" . . . to many a volunteer such comments brought disenchantment. It is one thing for a rebel to risk being hanged for the People. Quite another when the People is ready to cheer the hangman!

* * *

In London the noon temperature rose to near the eighty mark. Southend and Brighton reported record holiday crowds. Even the war-news seemed destined to be sunny.

In the morning papers there was no whisper of the stroke that had seized the sister capital, across the Irish sea. Instead, the reader was told of "the arrest of Sir R. Casement"—an announcement delayed two days by the censorship—and there was brief reference, too, to the crushing of "an Irish extremist plot." But even this encouraging development took second place to a phenomenon so often-hoped for in vain that its realisation came almost as a shock: as if Santa Claus had materialised before the eyes of half-doubting children.

Though, disconcertingly, they showed no signs of "snow on their boots", the Russians at last had arrived to aid the western front. They had landed in France—"their brown faces glowing with pleasure" at the cheers and floral tributes of the rapturous Marseille crowds. They had only one ambition

—according to their General and the scribes—and that was "to get to the fighting." Fervently it was hoped that their desire be speedily met.

On the Home Front, too, news had a lighter touch. A German Taube had circled Dover, and been "prevented" from dropping her bombs. "Holidaymakers," it was said, "had thoroughly enjoyed the show." The season's significance was certainly not lost on the caption writers. "Easter eggs for the Russian armies," was the way in which they described Austro-Hungarian reverses. But already Fleet Street was considering the implications, and the parentage, of a far less welcome type of "easter egg"—the monstrous thing that had been hatched so very much nearer home.

"Sinn Feiners"—the Mirror was to explain that the term meant "Irish malcontents"—had occupied St Stephen's Green, Dublin. "Mostly armed," they had seized the Post Office, and occupied houses in St Stephen's Green, Sackville Street, Abbey Street, and along the quays. The Chief Secretary had informed the House that "the situation was well in hand!"

To some, including an aghast General Friend, whose "courtesy call" on the Horse Guards had received (reputedly) an extremely rude reception, and had resulted in an urgent rush to get back to his Command by the very next boat, Augustine Birrell had produced a masterpiece of under- statement.

* * *

Well in hand? Lord Donoughmore, for one, could not believe it.

Driving into the city on Tuesday morning he was shocked to find "no soldiers or police." The streets everywhere were controlled by "the armed Sinn Feiners." He was wounded the following day; when in the "tranquil" countryside.

At about the time of Donoughmore's excursion, another Irish peer—the distinguished Lord Dunsany—had *his* own opportunity of assessing the strength of the "serious disturbances" in Dublin.

He was motoring into town in the company of an army officer, when ordered to halt by rebel pickets. His chauffeur accelerated, and immediately shots were fired.

One bullet cut Dunsany's cheek. Another hit the chauffeur in the hand. The army officer helped bring the car to a stop, and the thoroughly shaken trio were brought before the nearest rebel commander. Fortunately, he was an admirer of

Dunsany's poetry. "You are not yet for the glittering gates," he quoted, and set them free.

In general the Volunteers were no such respectors of persons. The car of Sir Horace Plunkett—a member of the Irish Privy Council noted for his sympathetic attitude to Home Rule—was shot at. The bullet drilled a hole through the chassis only a few inches from the driver's seat.

More tragic had been the fate of the 17-year-old son of the British army officer commanding the Magazine Fort in the Phoenix Park. Running to a neighbour's house to give warning of the rebel attack he was pursued and shot dead upon the doorstep.

However, despite these manifestations of what the Irish Office called "grave disturbances", a casual visitor to the Castle area early on Tuesday afternoon might have felt—had he ignored the ransacked ruins of the City Hall—that Mr Birrell's comment was not so very far from the mark.

Stretcher bearers had supplemented Miss Florence Williams's devoted work among the wounded. The dead were also decently out of view. The streets were empty of people. In the hush the cry of seagulls could be heard.

It was 2.40 p.m. precisely when this strange tranquillity was shattered—by the blast of 500 rifles, and Elliotson's machine-guns. Having taken the City Hall, and neutralised Mallin's force on Stephen's Green, the reinforced garrison was not to rest on its laurels. It had been ordered to stage a mass break-out.

Yelling wildly the 5th Royal Dublin Fusiliers, led by Second Lieutenant F. O'Neill, charged into Cork Hill, which contained the two surviving strongpoints of the rebels—the outfitter's shop and the offices of the Express and Mail.

It was a battle of the utmost ferocity. No quarter was asked for, or given.

The military, three times repulsed, went in with grenade and bayonet. There were twenty-two rebels in the newspaper offices. By the end of the fighting all twenty-two were dead . . .

The first of Lowe's "limited objectives" having been achieved, he decided to broaden his base in the West.

Kent, in the South Dublin Union, had long been under heavy attack from his old opponents of the Royal Irish Regiment, operating from Richmond Barracks directly to his south. He had succeeded in fulfilling the main task assigned him: the barracks had been masked and the Royal Irish had been prevented from breaking north and linking with the Curragh column at Kingsbridge. His second task, to harry the

82

column should it attempt to break out eastwards had been less well performed. With the meagre numbers available to him it was in fact, impossible. But recently, with the Royal Irish attacking even more fiercely than before, he had been forced to pull back his outposts, and concentrate his force. Now, under further pressure, and after desperate resistance, he moved the whole body to the Nurses's Home. This, it transpired, was to be a fateful move. The Home was strong structurally, and in a good position for defence: but, once inside, he was isolated from all contact with the rebel forces in the distilleries, to his left; and the Curragh force was able to cement its route to the Castle.

For the third time running, the defenders of the distilleries and Guinness's were fooled by the absence of a direct attack. They saw no sinister reason for this apparent lack of enterprise, but were content, once more, to stay put while they indulged in idle sniping at the occasional tommy who showed himself in the south; their preoccupation was to perfect their own defences. They appear to have had no idea of the strong force that, even now, was marching past them to the east. "As the British didn't attack," one of them later explained, "we thought we must be winning . . ."

The establishment of his east-west axis now almost complete, Lowe looked to the start of the drive from south to north. This would be conducted by the reinforcements promised from England. Already they were starting on their way.

CHAPTER SEVEN

Young Harry Bate was not around to see the first of the
English soldiers arrive in Kingstown Harbour. When the two
blacked-out ships that carried their advance guard crept
cautiously between the claws of the curving stone piers that
jutted out to the north of Scotsman's Bay, it was 10.30 at
night, and young Harry, at that hour, was securely tucked up
in bed. His grandfather, however, decided to wander down
to the railway jetty, and later returned to Eden Park with
somewhat troubled reflections. The soldiers, as he said next
morning, looked so *young*.

A point to be lost sight of by the end of the year—and
soon almost completely buried beneath the rebellion's
"national" legend—was that, until the arrival of these
reinforcements for the Crown, the fighting had been almost
exclusively between Irishmen. The Dublin Fusiliers . . . the
Royal Irish Rifles . . . the Royal Irish Regiment . . . the 3rd
and 6th Reserve Cavalry regiments . . . it was with these *Irish*
units, and others like them, that the Volunteers and the Citizen
Army men had been locked in combat for possession of the
city. The shot policemen had been Irish, and so were the
angry women. Irish too had been the elderly G.R.'s and the
college students who had fought the rebels from Trinity. It
was only now, on the night of Tuesday 26th, when the tide
of battle was already well on the turn, that the " Saxon Foe "
of tradition set foot on Irish soil. For one with such an
unpleasant reputation he did not look particularly ferocious.

The troops who began to disembark at Kingstown, belonged
to the 78th Brigade, of the 59th Division, and were as English
as the best of their enemies would wish them. They came
from the shires and industrial cities of the North: South
Staffs, North Staffs, and "Robin Hoods", the Sherwood
Foresters. But though—in the mythology of rebellion—they
were to go down as "battle-seasoned regulars", defied by
patriot amateurs, there was little about these soldiers that
merited such a distinction. In actual fact, the vast majority
had seen less than twelve weeks' training, and most of them
were youngsters, under twenty.

The 59th was no first-line division. Its primary role had
been to act as a training unit; and as such it was continually

being drained of drafts for France. Its secondary function was for home defence, to act as a sort of watchdog against a German invasion. Its new commitment, to crush "Sinn Fein" rebellion in Southern Ireland, had arisen purely by accident . . . it had happened to be handy.

Positioned near Watford, the division had the advantage of excellent rail communications. Except for its courage, it had very little else. It boasted not a single hand grenade; and few of its private soldiers had ever handled one. Its ammunition ran to less than 50 rounds a man, for rifles that in many cases were made in Japan. Mr Reginald Bate— though no military expert—had good reason to feel concerned.

* * *

It was immediately after breakfast when Harry and his grandfather went down to the coast road to see the 59th assemble for the march on Dublin.

Some of the men had been seasick. All of them were still shaken by the speed of their transplantation. Less than 24 hours before they had been called, without explanation, from Easter Leave. They had been brought from their homes in the North, the high-life in London, the cinemas and pubs of Hertfordshire to be packed into a train and driven northward, embarked—still without explanation—on ships that seemed to be in such a hurry to get going that machine-guns and artillery had to be left behind on the quay.

The Commanding Officer of the 2/8th Sherwood Foresters had protested at the time about some aspects of bureaucracy's nervous haste. Each of his men had been issued at Liverpool with 120 rounds of ball ammunition, field dressings, and iodine capsules—"in the latter case as far as they would go" —but he'd been told that his group of Lewis guns would have to stay ashore.

"But they could be invaluable," he had reasonably argued.

"*Men* are wanted over there, not guns . . ." had been the irritable reply.

However, despite this unpromising start to their voyage, and their being dumped in full marching-order on this unfamiliar shore, the troops were in high spirits; still further exalted by the warmth of an Irish welcome.

Until they had docked, the vast majority had no idea of where they were going, or why. And, even now, the "why" eluded them. The thought of all this fuss being due to an Irish "rebellion" seemed to smack as much of Gilbert and Sullivan as, say, an S.O.S. to put down insurrection in Birmingham.

Such things just did not happen—not in the British Isles. Nor did their reception help make the young soldiers any wiser. On the quayside a paperseller hawked news of revolutionary violence: but ashore they encountered a positive riot of loyalty.

Groups of well-wishers from the town, and neighbouring Blackrock, had been gathering since dawn to see the troops on their way. Now, as the 2/8th began its march it found itself besieged by individual kindness. As the troops received the order March-at-ease, cigarettes and sweets were pressed upon them. Local residents came out with jugs of tea. Bewildered by such friendliness and delighted at their apparently happy role of liberators the tommies began to enjoy themselves. This wasn't going to be a bad war after all.

It was when another battalion in the column was about to move that a note of discord was struck: struck by the terse command of an officer, repeated down the ranks.

Young Harry did not catch what was being said, but was aware of a sudden change of manner among the troops, and a sudden distress among those near him in the crowd. A woman standing beside him held up to a passing soldier a basket of fruit. He pushed it rudely aside. "Thanks, ma'am, but I'm not so daft. I don't trust bloody sinn feiners!"

The woman flushed with hurt, then again offered the fruit. But the next file, equally sullen, looked to their front and ignored her. The woman turned away, and so did other civilians. There was a general muttering of dissatisfaction, to which Mr Reginald Bate contributed. And young Harry, to his pleasure and surprise, found himself the possessor of both the basket and the fruit.

"*You* might as well have them, love," said the elderly donor sadly. "For one thing's sure, the soldiers won't even look at them!" There were tears in her eyes, he noticed with astonishment. She had gone before he could remember his manners, and say thanks.

"Idiots!" said his grandfather. "Blethering idiots!"

"What's up, man?" asked a neighbour, a new arrival.

"The soldiers are saying," said Harry's grandfather heavily, "that their officers have ordered them not to take food and drink. They say it could be a plot to poison them." He paused, and then, with unwonted anger, added: "Poison! They must be out of their minds! Who ever heard of an Irishman stooping to poison? Why in the devil's name, do they always make the same mistakes? Why don't they send people here who know something about the country?"

Poison!

Young Harry Bate looked dubiously at the fruit basket, and then, extracting a particularly rosy apple, he decided to throw all caution to the winds.

"Poison" or not, that apple tasted good.

* * *

Wednesday morning marked the start of a whole series of tactical moves by the Crown Forces. The aggressive action prepared by Lowe was now at last to be implemented.

At about the same time as the spearhead of the 59th Division mustered to begin its thrust from the south, a battalion of the Royal Irish Rifles completed its movement to outflank the sorely-pressed Union and break through to St Stephen's Green from the west. North of the river, from the east, troops landed on North Wall would drive towards O'Connell Street, to link hands, if all went well, with units attempting to infiltrate the central rebel position from the rear. And meanwhile, on the Liffey, a group of seamen stood to action stations aboard His Majesty's ship *Hecla*.

The *Hecla*'s presence was fortuitous: but none the less welcome for that. She had put into Dublin on a routine visit on Monday night, in complete ignorance of the turn events had taken in the city. In fact she was about to tie-up when her curiosity was aroused by the unexpected crackle of rifle-fire near the electricity power station. This phenomenon she had gone to investigate, and, in so doing, had at last received a signal from the Castle.

Since then the *Hecla* had been of service to the Crown in many ways. She had played her searchlights on the quaysides, dispersing rebel groups there. She had raked their lines of approach with rifles and machine-guns. She had provided a communication link between the troops on both sides of the river. But the one thing she had not done was to use her guns: to shell a British city was not the Navy's job. Now, however, this restriction had been relaxed. As a prelude to the attack from North Wall, the rebels were to be chased from their eastern outposts. Liberty Hall, said intelligence reports, was held in force: it was essential that the military had artillery support.

Hecla's commander was not too happy about the target. It was one that was easy to see, but promised to be difficult to hit. The trouble was to get at it without destroying a lot of property in the process. The Gunner would have to lay the gun to fire *under* the massive railway bridge that linked

Westland Row and Amiens Street Stations. With good luck he might send the shell between the water and the arch. With bad—"Will the old girl bring down the blooming bridge?" asked one of the gun team.

At 8 a.m. the *Hecla* opened fire.

* * *

The echo of the warship's gun, hurled back and magnified by the Iron Bridge and the Customs House, resounded across North Side, and brought people running to their doors and windows in time to see a stream of refugees begin to debouch from the houses near Beresford Square. Almost careless by now to the constant crackle of musketry, they'd been terrified out of their wits by the wail and the whine and the crunch of the first shells. They were also bewildered, and hurt in heart as well as nerve. The Navy—*their* Navy—it was terrible that it should do this to them. To these men and women, and their crying children, the bombardment seemed, in this moment of panic, as though it was aimed at them personally; designed to claim them as victims. The Navy—*their* Navy—things seemed too bad to be true.

"Naval guns, Ma," said one of Mrs Spellman's rescued soldiers, emerging, razor in hand, from the bathroom. "Take my word for it, it's all up with the shinners now . . ."

She did not answer. She felt sick with horror and grief. The soldier misunderstood the reason for her silence. "Hey, cheer up now—they're not going to shoot at *you!*"

But still Mrs Spellman was too upset to reply.

Of course, she had no use at all for those reckless and ruthless Sinn Feiners. If they knew that she was daring to harbour her two soldiers chances were, she thought, she would be murdered in her bed: but, all the same, some of them were mere boys. This booming cannonade made the whole thing unfair. Quite suddenly, the ogre-like appearances and proportions with which, subconsciously, she had endowed the wretched rebels, underwent a startling metamorphosis. In their place arose a vision perhaps equally overdrawn, of a shepherd boy with a sling standing alone on a plain in Israel.

She snapped back to reality, and glanced at the clock. It was shortly after eighty-thirty. Breakfast-time. She would best compose herself, and put on the rashers. And then she remembered that there were no rashers left. Nor was there any bread: the bakery on the corner had run out of stocks the previous day. They would have to put up with porridge.

As from now, it would be porridge for breakfast, dinner and tea.

Mrs Spellman looked out of the window and felt her eyes fill again at the fright of the children, running across the square. What havoc would the guns wreak upon her beloved city, before men came to their senses once again?

Once more, she turned for reassurance to the portrait of Queen Victoria, in place of honour over the mantelshelf, and then doubled up with a fervent prayer to St Patrick; to save not only herself and her soldier charges, but everyone else caught up in this suffering Dublin, wracked by a strife that so few could comprehend.

*   *   *

Kitty Francis, in the Shelbourne, also heard the *Hecla*'s guns. But this time she did *not* look out to see what it was about. Miss Francis had been cured of looking-out. The rebels who had been driven from the Green, and were now holding out in the College of Surgeons, had recovered much of their former aggressive spirit. Seeking the elusive machine-gunners, they had reduced practically every window in the hotel to a heap of fine powdered glass. "Relieved" the hotel was supposed to have been with the advent of the British picquets. To Miss Francis, and others, such a "relief" was pretty comfortless. Siege restrictions were now in force in Dublin's smartest and most exclusive hotel. The liquor in the Long Bar merely mocked with its abundance, the almost complete absence of water. The foyer was stacked with rifles and revolvers. To walk out of the front door was to court sudden death. She had had her fill of Dublin. She wished she were home.

*   *   *

Into the garden of Dublin Castle came a young V.A.D. in search of air. She had been working in the sterilising room and then had lent a hand in the wards. She had been working for 24 hours with no more than half an hour's break. The stink of chloroform and iodine had turned her stomach. Momentarily she paused, as she heard the echo of the *Hecla*'s guns, and then her attention focused on the men by the garden wall.

There were twenty of them, and at first she thought that they were digging trenches. It was only when she spoke to an officer she knew, that she realised the "trenches" were graves. The ones nearest her were reserved for officers and behind them were two deep pits which, her friend informed her, were for "the men." One of them was for the military dead; the other for the rebels.

Burials would be conducted at night. Things were getting organised.

* * *

From the horrors taking place behind them in the city, one group of volunteers had so far been divorced—the group commanded by George Reynolds in Clanwilliam House, Lower Mount Street.

After their initial brush with the unfortunate G.R.'s—they had been genuinely shaken to find that their targets had been unarmed—the insurgents had continued with their efficient job of fortification. Now, like their comrades in the advance posts in Northumberland Road, they had nothing left to do except to wait.

The morning sun glittered on the still canal. The long straight road beyond the hump-backed bridge was seemingly lifeless. From where Reynolds stood, at the window of the lofty drawing room, not even the dust appeared to stir, and he commented approvingly on the positioning of the outposts, and the discipline observed by those who manned them.

Grace and Malone in No 25 . . . O'Donoghue and his detachment in Robert's Yard . . . the snipers in the Parochial Hall . . . for all that could be seen of them they might as well have been so many wraiths.

Daffodils stood like sentries on the turned verges of trim lawns. Blinds masked the windows of the tall houses that lay beyond them, twin rows of respectability stretching as far as the eye could see.

Crouched over their rifles, the Clanwilliam men awaited their enemy. The world before them seemed somehow strangely unreal. They looked out on it as travellers, about to pass it by. The silence was deep. They could almost hear it.

CHAPTER EIGHT

"It was a glorious morning and Ireland looked her best, which is saying a great deal, and one at least of us who knew her well, felt sad at the prospect before the Battalion. . . ."

Such were the words with which Lt. Colonel Coape-Oates, a veteran of the Boer War and the Mons Retreat, and an Irishman with unshakeable love of country, was to describe the start of his command's march to the north, and the bloodiest of all the tragedies that the rising was to carry in its wake.

Though with shoulders bowed beneath the weight of their packs and slung Lee-Enfields, and all the paraphernalia of British full marching-order, the young "Sherwoods" of the 178th Brigade still continued to sing as they left Kingstown behind them and pressed on towards the city. Four battalions strong, forming the 59th's spearhead, they marched on almost parallel lines towards the barrier of the canals.

Oates's battalion, the 2/8th took the Coast Road, with the sparkling sea to their right. Ahead of them were their rivals the 2/7th, commanded by Lt. Colonel Cecil Fane, C.M.G., D.S.O., and, like Oates, a veteran. The remaining two battalions took the inland route, the Stillorgan-Donnybrook road, half a mile towards the west.

Three hours earlier, in the temporary divisional H.Q. that had been established in the Yacht Club, the officers had been given a briefing of a nature unprecedented to "Home Forces" operating in a part of the United Kingdom. They had been told to exercise, during their six-mile march, the precautions of a force passing through hostile territory. Each company must provide a platoon to cover side-roads and corner dwellings, and another platoon was to search suspect houses and gardens. In the event, however, this discipline proved difficult to maintain.

It was hard—almost impossible—for young soldiers to feel, in these gracious boulevards, the sense of urgency, and apprehension of imminent danger, that would have characterised a similar approach through, say, the ruins of an enemy-held town in Flanders, or the lunar landscape of the Persian Gulf.

All that the English lads had so far sniffed of the much

talked-about "rebellion", was that parliament had been told it was pretty well under control. All they had seen of "rebels" since their landing, had been two youths on the jetty, who had shot at them with nothing more lethal than a string of rude words: kid's stuff to what the Robin Hoods were used to. The precautions to be observed when approaching corner houses smacked embarrassingly of a tuppenny blood mentality: particularly in view of the nature of the district. Why, every corner they passed seemed to be a grandstand for the loyalists, an assembly point for retired officers and their ladies, out to pay nostalgic tribute to the Crown.

The same atmosphere of unreality that had been noticed by Knight and others as characterising the commencement of the rebellion hung over this parade of the English columns sent to terminate it. Even to this day, survivors of the force recall with near-incredulity the lightheartedness with which they began their enterprise, so soon to erupt in bloody action. For the Sherwoods, there was to be no gradual transition between the ordered environment of normal civilised living and the lunatic chaos of the battlefield: the dividing line was to be all too sharply drawn.

Some shops were still open along the route, and at one point an agricultural show functioned in all its glory, with county gentry and their wives rubbing shoulders with farmers and socialites as casually as though the city that lay burning to the north was as remote and impersonal in its impact on their lives as, say, Kut-el-Amara, where Townshend was making his last stand against the Turks.

Generosity continued to be lavish. As the battalion passed a group of bystanders near Ballsbridge, an elderly man ran into the road and presented one of the officers with a pair of binoculars. "They may come in useful," he said, ". . . the only gift I could think of."

But the oddest—and certainly the most poignant—memory retained by the Sherwoods today is the delight of their Assistant Adjutant—Captain F. C. Dietrichsen—at seeing his two children wave to the column from the kerb. Unbeknown to him, they had been sent to Ireland, to holiday with their grandmother.

Hearing their cries of "Daddy", the normally rather staid and serious Dietrichsen so far forgot himself as to break rank and embrace them.

He was to die within the hour.

"He's coming!"

Roused from the briefest of cat-naps by the Volunteer sentry's shout, Reynolds rushed to a first-floor window of Clanwilliam House, and stared in the direction of Northumberland Road, and the spot where its straightness was broken by the curve that led into Haddington Road and, on the west side, Malone and Grace's position in number 25. The sun glittered on steel.

Reynolds looked again. Beneath the glitter were two minute blobs of khaki. He focused his field-glasses, and the blobs became men. Advance scouts of the English, with rifles at the port, and bayonets fixed.

He told his men to stand by.

* * *

Brigadier's Lowe's responsibility was almost unprecedented for one of his comparatively junior rank. In Friend's absence, he had become almost the de facto G.O.C., and at the same time was in tactical command of the forces engaged in the battle for Dublin. These forces were formidable in themselves, and the complexities involved in their deployment might well have awed a less confident officer than this professional cavalryman.

They consisted of the garrison of the city, over four battalions strong, the 25th Irish infantry brigade which he had brought in from the Curragh, the Curragh mobile (cavalry) column, nearly 2,000 strong, and, as an additional insurance, a substantial force from Ulster.

Now, with the arrival of the troops from England, the rebels' ruin was certain and sure. The 59th, although its strength had not yet been fully deployed, could add another twelve battalions to the numerical odds that ran so heavily in favour of the Crown. The trap was about to shut.

In planning the Sherwoods' route of march, Lowe hoped to repeat, on a south to north axis, the success he had already achieved in the drive from west to east. While Kent's men had been locked in valiant battle with the Royal Irish, he had by-passed the chain of strongpoints formed by the distilleries and Guinness's in order to reach the Castle and Stephen's Green and lodge himself, so to speak, in the heart of rebel communications south of the river. The 59th's march would be similarly conducted; and de Valera's main contingent, in Boland's Mill, would not be attacked direct, but be outflanked and isolated. What was needed was to storm the O'Connell Street junta's fortress. This effected, the other posts

93

would die almost automatically: so many limbs of an uprooted tree.

Yet incredibly, even at this late hour, the stubborn rebels were refusing to give up hope. In fact, in the Four Courts area, they could even claim a victory.

*   *   *

"Sure, if we'd drums and standards, and all the rest of the trimmings," quipped one of the men in green, "we'd have turned out in style, to give you the honours of war . . ."

For British soldiers, the prisoners were a very mixed bag indeed. Some of them were veterans, and bore themselves as such, while others, pale-faced youngsters, were be-spectacled, round-shouldered, and endowed with a studious slouch. Their buttons hadn't seen a shine for the past three days and more. Their hair was dishevelled, and of unsoldierlike length. As they were marched off to confinement in the Four Courts, they differed about the step.

All the same, the ribbing to which they were subjected by their captors was, on the whole, good-natured and tinged with a certain respect.

For this was the climax of a siege that had lasted for forty-eight hours. A siege where each side had done its solemn duty, and neither had suffered the loss of a drop of blood.

One of the objectives of Daly's men had been a British Army barracks, close to the northwestern quays and only a street or two away from Riley's Fort. It was not, at first sight, an attractive prize to aim at: the Linenhall Barracks was probably the oldest in Ireland. Nor did it house an enemy likely to threaten the rebel lines: its sole garrison was a detachment of the Army Pays Corps. It was its geographical position that gave the place any importance: and then only in the context of the time. Should the Crown Forces contrive to filter through reinforcements, they might use it to get astride the route between the Four Courts and the Post Office.

There were only fifty troops in the Linenhall's "garrison", and most of them were elderly, C.3, or merely boys. Yet when the volunteers demanded their surrender, these clerkly soldiers had shown martial mettle—and refused. They were quite determined: they would hold out to the end.

As it was known that the sole armament of the intrepid force consisted of a clumsy service revolver, it had not seemed to the rebels that this "end" would be long deferred. Events had since proved them wrong.

Realising the futility of attempting a pitched battle, the

94

Pay Corps men had fixed on another way of delaying their enemy's triumph. Displaying an originality in the face of impossible odds that was certainly not of the type commended by traditional military text-books, the fifty had retired behind the stout brick of the barracks then slammed the doors behind them, and locked themselves in!

Only now had they reached the limit of endurance, after causing their victors the maximum inconvenience. Bullets had been useless against the thickness of their fortress. Pickaxes and sledgehammers had been employed in vain. The Pay Corps had surrendered only when the rebels—with an ingenuity equal to their own—had employed a charge of gelignite, and blown down the walls upon them.

* * *

While Lowe stretched his long legs, in their glittering riding boots, amid the tapestry, chairs and piled carpets of the Royal Hospital, Kilmainham—home of the Irish "pensioners", and the G.O.C. Ireland—remote Westminster resounded to the sound of verbal warfare. As he issued the orders designed to isolate the rebels in so many separate boxes, each surrounded by a wall of death, the Brigadier's voice was gentlemanly, and his manner almost casual. In Westminster, they had no such brief for the cadences of courtesy.

In the Commons, Pemberton-Billing—the airman M.P. whose suggestions for the furtherance of the war effort were sometimes considered to go a bit too far—gave for once but a feeble echo of popular indignation when he asked for an assurance that Casement (that traitor!) would "be shot forthwith."

Shot! In general, the mood was such that the bulk of P.B.'s constituents would probably have favoured Sir Roger's being hanged, drawn and quartered, or whatever else was necessary to ensure that he sustained the maximum of pain. Nor was this feeling confined exclusively to the English. In Drogheda, Volunteers mobilised—but purely to offer their services in support of the Crown Forces. In the Loos sector, where Irish infantry were confronted by German pleas to "avenge Dublin, and join us", they answered with a vicious attack that settled their would-be "friends and brothers" with the bayonet. A "shinner" was, in the public mind, synonymous with "traitor." A fact that no man appreciated more bitterly than the temporarily disregarded Arthur Griffith.

* * *

Monday and Tuesday had passed in an agony of frustration for the man whose slogan—Sinn Fein—had once provided the common rallying cry for nationalists of all classes, and all shades of religious belief; and those earnest study, and romantic appreciation, of a revolution in Hungary in the century past, had now been converted into bloody battle in the Georgian squares and crescents of the city he loved so well.

For Arthur Griffith, the Rising was at once the triumphant crystallisation in action of the national spirit he had resurrected and refurbished, and the heart-breaking rejection of the method, timing, and objective, that he had persistently urged upon followers more and more inclined to take their own sweet way. He had striven for a free and completely independent Ireland in which the consciences of radicals and royalists alike could have been reconciled by the device of a dual monarchy. And instead, he had now got a "provisional republic", and a rising launched in the face of his bitter resistance, at a time, when to him, it was obviously doomed to failure . . . a rising that had split, and therefore might well ruin, the entire structure of the nationalist organisation, and perpetuate the division of Irishmen into opposing camps.

Yet by Wednesday, when he could see his major fears being realised, and the Irish cause being identified—to the delight of its enemies—with wholesale conspiracy as traitor-puppet for the Kaiser, this dedicated and deeply religious man, who carried a rosary in his pocket and had never been known to swear, could identify himself only with his country's fighting past. Resolved to sink his differences with the insurgent leaders, he appealed to them to allow him to help in the defence of the Post Office. It was a request that was received with some embarrassment.

Griffith wanted no part in the direction of the rising. He wanted—now that the die had been cast—to share in the sacrifice and suffering that he knew would be its inevitable first consequence. He was ready to serve in any capacity the new men might choose to decide, but preferably he wished to fight as a humble volunteer. It was not to be.

Few could have been unmoved by this heartfelt plea of the Sinn Fein leader. Though his policy had been ignored, and Connolly in particular distrusted his philosophy, the sincerity of the man was not questioned, nor was his steel-true spirit. But both Pearse and Connolly, despite their outward show of confidence in the progress of the rising, were already considering the consequences of a nationalist defeat, particularly as regards its implications for the future of the movement. Should the rebellion be crushed it was evident that they themselves could expect short shrift. Pearse's dreams of martyrdom looked like becoming accomplished fact.

Before acquiring his highly controversial status—President of a republic declared without a vote, and Commander in Chief of an army that had deposed its former officers—Pearse had written a poem that, more than any other item of evidence, may provide the key to his, and Connolly's, philosophy towards the insurrection, and explain their reaction to their former mentor's offer of service:

"The wise have pitied the fool that hath striven
    to give a life
  In the world of time and space among the hulks
    of actual things,
  To a dream that was dreamed in the heart, and
    that only the heart could hold.
  O wise men riddle me this: what if the dream
    come true?
  What if the dream come true? And if millions
    unborn shall dwell
  In the house that I shaped in my heart, the
    noble house of my thought?
  Lord, I have staked my soul, I have staked
    the lives of my kin
  On the truth of thy dreadful word. Do not
    remember my failures
  But remember this my faith . . ."

Who would remember the "faith" of Padraic Pearse—he may have reflected—were none left free to capitalise upon the method of his dying. Exploiting it for the sake of the "dream dreamed in the heart"? To many, at present, that "dream" was far more like a nightmare. Yet, for its realisation, he had indeed "staked the lives" of his kin. Was the sacrifice to prove fruitless?

It would appear that—on Wednesday—both Pearse and Connolly agreed that Sinn Fein's commitment to the rising must, for the present, be kept to the minimum. Only this way could it be free to use the affair as propaganda symbol for the future.

"Sorry, but we prefer you to stay outside," went the terse reply to Griffith. The prestige of his name would have been invaluable to the rebels at the beginning of the rising. Now he, like O'Neill, must continue to fret in exile.

*   *   *

By Wednesday noon, O'Connell Street had greatly changed in appearance. Even the most fanatical devotee of the physical force policy would scarcely have said for the better.

Through a sky lightly veiled by the smoke that rose from Liberty Hall, to the left, and a gutted strongpoint on the flank of the Four Courts, to the right, bullets whirred and whined and rattled tiles and chimneys. From the Post Office stretched an apron of barbed wire across a pavement that, except for the occasional rebel runner, was empty of life or movement. A tram lay overturned in front of Nelson's Pillar. Displayed along the side of what had once been its upper deck was an advertisement for Bovril. Among the citizens "that sinking feeling" was much in evidence.

North of the Parnell Monument the looters were still active, but their numbers had dramatically decreased. To cross the southern end of the street was an adventure of deadly hazard. The snipers in Trinity, across the river, had been reinforced by a detachment from the Castle. A woman had been shot dead outside Kelly's, on the corner of O'Connell Bridge.

To the north, however, small groups of people still congregated. Driven together by the need for information, or the desire to seek comfort for their fears, they chatted and argued with the sort of nervous volubility that was later to characterise Londoners in the blitz. At the moment, the Number One topic was the fate of Nelson's Pillar. Sandbags had been stacked around its base, and enquirers had been told that the rebels' "engineers" were planting gelignite, to blow it up. The *Hecla*'s action was feared to be only a foretaste of worse to come. In the event of a naval bombardment, the tall pillar would give the gunlayers a convenient ranging-mark.

Oddly, considering the circumstances, the precaution shocked and dismayed quite a few of the citizens. Preoccupied though they might be with their own unfortunate plight, these unpredictable folk took umbrage at the idea of such explosive vandalism. Nelson's Pillar was so much a part of the everyday Dublin scene that the idea of anyone attempting to remove it was received with a sense of personal outrage.

Mrs Spellman was particularly upset, and expressed her sense of shame to her two young soldier charges. On the whole, however, they took the news rather coolly. "That will be a smack in the eye for poor old Emma," said one of them with a grin.

Mrs Spellman thought the remark in bad taste, and did not hesitate to say so. But after all, she later reflected, you couldn't really expect these English tommies to care. Dublin was not their home. What was Nelson to them!

* * *

While the fate of his monument was being so hotly debated on the shore, the representative of the navy the little Admiral had led to The Three Great Victories was again trailing her coat on the dark waters of the Liffey.

The *Hecla* was enjoying an active day. She had been fired on by rebel snipers, and had answered with machine-guns. She had dispersed a detachment on the march and had given support to an infantry attack. Despite the cramped conditions in which she operated, which meant that she was always within range of enemy fire, morale was high—and rose even higher at the news that was spreading ashore concerning the fate of her target of the morning, Liberty Hall.

The Labour H.Q. was said to have been crowded with rebels at the time the gunboat began her shoot. They had run like rats, informants told her officers. James Connolly had appeared on the top of the steps in an effort to rally them, and had been killed by an exploding shell.

Connolly dead! This was news indeed, and went the rounds with startling speed. Even though the degree of heroism displayed by the victim on his demise varied with the political complexion of the several "eye-witnesses", the story was almost universally believed. Despite the report of the assault party of infantry that had followed up the bombardment, and found not a sign of rebels—living or dead—it spread far beyond the confines of the city and began to circulate in London. Soon the Mirror was publishing the story as the lead in what it called "the true facts about the rebellion."

It was unfortunate for the Crown Forces—and perhaps, in the long run, for the rebels too—that Connolly himself, that stubbornest of men, refused to accept the news as gospel. Far from being a corpse, buried beneath the ruins of Liberty Hall, he was busy in the Post Office, stumping around the defence posts and repeating cheerfully to everyone he saw, "They're beaten, by God. They're beaten!"

With Plunkett so ill that he now lay in semi-delirium, and Pearse absorbed in compiling yet another manifesto, the Labour leader had attained a terrific status among the young

99

volunteers. They turned to him as a father figure, the fount of power and comfort. At the crack of the *Hecla*'s guns, doubt had begun to creep into the minds of the rank-and-file —and Connolly knew it. He must put heart into the youngsters —tell them only what they wanted so desperately to hear. And this he did : with great effectiveness.

Few of those who brightened at the approach of this rugged and intrepid propagandist of optimism, remembered, as they snatched at his assurances, his oft-repeated assertion in the past. "They'll never use artillery. It might destroy capitalist property!"

* * *

Leaving his home at Eden Park, Mr Reginald Bate mounted his bicycle and began to pedal slowly towards the city. His anxiety about the safety of his office and the cherished files therein had removed the last vestige of his professional caution. At all costs he must find out what was *really* happening in the Post Office, instead of being dependent on rumours that, to his way of thinking, were becoming every moment more horrific and unreal.

Mr Bate was approaching Ballsbridge when two ambulances passed him, travelling at speed. A hundred yards or so further on, two young English soldiers stepped with bayonets fixed into the road and gestured him to a stop. He could go no farther they said. All civilian traffic was banned.

Mr Bate started to lodge a formal protest, then saw, over the trees the menacing grey-black smoke that stained the sky to the north and decided to argue no longer. As he turned his bike he was startled by an outburst of violent rifle fire, from only a few hundred yards away.

It increased in volume and intensity, until it echoed through the quiet suburb like an electric storm.

Mr Bate pedalled home.

"Those villains," he said to Harry, "are destroying Dublin."

For the first time, the boy saw his grandfather on the verge of tears.

Several minutes passed before young Harry raised the question he had been dying to ask since he had waved goodbye to the long columns of soldiers, commencing their march from the harbour.

"Have our men beaten the rebels yet?" he asked.

Mr Bate sighed. "There has been some fighting Harry, in Westmoreland Road so I'm told." He brooded for a moment, perhaps thinking of his sons, so far from home. Of Reg, now in North China . . . of Alfred, now fighting in the Flanders mud . . . and Edwin, serving as a doctor in the R.A.M.C. And then he forced himself to brighten up. "We'll look on this as a holiday, my boy. We'll go and picnic somewhere."

The boy squatting on the cushion on the crossbar, they took the road to the shore, where the surge of the sea drowned the echoes of the battle now raging to their north.

CHAPTER NINE

Erect as a ramrod, immensely tall, and made even more
conspicuous by his gleaming brown riding boots and fawn
coloured British warm—worn in splendid disregard of the
blazing sunshine—Lt Colonel Cecil Fane stabbed a gloved
forefinger on the map-case, and said to his company
commanders, clustering around him: "Gentlemen, we have a
thousand yards to go!"

On such a beautiful morning it all seemed rather unreal.

There were two water obstacles in the way of the advance
from the south. One of them was the river Dodder, to the
north of Ballsbridge itself. The other was the canal. Vane,
in the van with the 2/7th, had been braced for action as the
column had approached the bridge over the Dodder. With
no fewer than five roads converging on its approaches, the
spot was a bottleneck; a natural for defence; but already
the river lay well to the Sherwoods' rear; not a single sniper
had contested their approach. It was on the second obstacle
that Fane's attention was now riveted: on the map, a thin
blue line; the canal.

A few dozen yards from where the officers conferred, the
walls of the weedgrown grounds of a large mansion—
seemingly uninhabited—marked the junction of Northumberland Road and Pembroke Avenue; turning off to the left at
an angle of 45 degrees and leading up towards Baggot Street
bridge, twin of the Sherwoods' projected crossing point, and
a third of a mile to its left.

Dead ahead, up the broad straight swathe of prim
Northumberland Road itself, a gap in the even spacing of the
tall lamp standards that bordered the well-swept pavements,
marked the point where the Haddington Road bisected from
west to east the battalion's line of advance. But the slightest
of slight curves, and the bulge of the evergreens that hedged
the Victorian houses prevented the men from seeing the top
half of the road, the stretch that included Number 25, the
Parochial Hall, and the hump-backed canal bridge, with
Clanwilliam House behind it.

Fane glanced again at the map, and the black cube ringed
by crayon that lay to the immediate south-east of the bridge,
and therefore to the right of his column's projected route.
"Gentlemen, Mount Street Schools . . ."

No one present failed to appreciate the significance of the phrase.

An intelligence report had been circulated by H.Q. It stated that the Schools had been occupied by the rebels. The Sherwoods would meet resistance there. It must be overcome . . .

As the brief conference broke up, sparrows fought in a nearby garden for bread thrown to them by the halted tommies. From the dormer window of a house a maid servant peeped cautiously through the curtains, then withdrew as the soldiers blew her kisses. From behind the trees in the grounds of the mansion at the junction of Pembroke Road, blue smoke rose tiredly from a bonfire of last year's leaves.

"It all seems so odd . . . a scrap in a place like this," said one of the company commanders. "With the English street names and so, it could almost be Home!"

His colleague repeated thoughtfully: "A thousand yards to go."

Neither knew of the grave omissions of the report on which the battalion's plans were based. Neither knew that, while the Schools had no longer to be reckoned with—they had been deserted by their "garrison" several hours before—the route that led to them was lined with three rebel strongpoints. And one of them was the mansion immediately to their front: Carisbrooke House.

Within minutes of resuming their advance the Sherwoods were enduring their baptism of fire.

* * *

The shots came from the grounds of the mansion, but were incredibly wildly aimed; and, after initial confusion, the young solders reacted like veterans. They scattered from the pavement, and fanned out; then, led by their officers, attacked with the bayonet under a heavy blanket of fire. Within minutes it was all over. The rebels—remnants of a Blackrock unit that had abandoned the House itself, against orders, the night before—were in flight.

Tails high at this success, the Sherwoods re-grouped and pressed on towards the north. Observing the cautious routine recommended for street fighting, they moved forward in what one spectator has since described as "a kind of stately dance".

First one detachment would advance on the right hand side of the road. Then, rifles at the ready, it would halt, and be passed by another, moving on the left. A third detachment would then move up, to give both groups covering fire; and the right hand detachment would start on the next lap of the march. At St Mary's Road, last turning to the left before the wide junction at the Haddington Road this order of advance was further improved upon. A platoon was moved up to occupy the houses on the corner. Considering the rawness of the youngsters, Fane thought they were shaping very well. It was at this moment that Reynolds centred the Sherwoods in his field glasses.

*   *   *

At the time the British advance scouts came into view the rebel defence plans were looking pretty sick, and a lesser man than Reynolds might well have turned in his command.

Grace and Malone, in Number 25, should have had a full section at their back. Instead, the section had gone missing —and intended to remain so. They had appealed for reinforcements, and had been spared two untrained boys. Both of the lads were under fifteen, and Malone—his conscience troubled—had sent them home again.

Again, Carisbrooke House was to have been held by a full company—and held with resolution. The defection of the Blackrock men could have incalculable consequences. Should the British decide to switch their plan for an advance via Mount Street Bridge, they would now be free to move up Pembroke Avenue, and advance via Baggot Street Bridge. They might cross the canal virtually unopposed, and at one blow outflank the whole of the south-eastern defences, sewing up de Valera's forces in a sack.

But almost the last straw for Reynolds had been when he discovered that the schools across the canal bridge to his left had been evacuated. He would have sent part of his own force to occupy them, but one of his youngsters had been so demoralised at the news of the British advance that he had sacked him for fear that his fright would spread. The Clanwilliam House garrison had now been reduced to seven.

Once more he focused his glasses on the khaki smudges, advancing slowly in file in line with the tall lamp standards that flanked the wide street.

Simultaneously, from Number 25, there came the swift burst of automatic fire. The two scouts seemed to falter, throw up their arms and fall.

Reynolds put aside the glasses, and picked up his Howth mauser. He set the sight at 300 yards. Then ordered: "Open Fire!"

*   *   *

"There was no question of an ambush," the historian of the 2/7th was later to record. To many of those on the spot it must have seemed remarkably like one.

Grace and Malone had waited until the troops had approached within twenty yards, and then had opened up with what was in fact the tommy gun of the day, the fully automatic Mauser machine-carbine.

Dietrichsen, the adjutant, perhaps thinking—who knows? —of that goodbye to his children outside Kingstown, was one of the first to fall. Caught in the stream of bullets, the young soldiers behind him momentarily panicked.

Fane jumped into the middle of the road, steadied the stampeding men, and yelled at the left hand files to get into the lee of the houses. But, as they did so, they were raked by the rifles of the Clanwilliam garrison. Completely bewildered, they fell flat among the front gardens, seeking cover among the fences and evergreens. Fane joined them, equally foxed by the source of this persistent fusilade, then remembered the intelligence report. "Oblique fire from the schools on the right of the road," he briefly—and wrongly—classified.

The whereabouts of the "machine-guns"—the automatics of Grace and Malone—still fretted him, however; and in default of anything clearer to aim at, he ordered rapid-fire on the houses on both sides of the street. And then at last —the rebel position located—he leaped to his feet, drew his sword, and led his troops to the charge.

Cheering wildly, two score of the Sherwoods followed the colonel forward. They dashed at the barricaded house with terrific courage, and then their ranks broke—to wither and die to the burst of the mauser bullets and the redoubled fury of the riflemen on the canal.

Both of the men in Number 25 aimed and fired at the tall Colonel, who suddenly reeled to a bullet in the arm. Yet again Fane jumped into the centre of the road, and stayed there until the assault party's survivors had once more reached the precarious shelter of the gardens. Then, while his wound was being dressed, he ordered a new tactic.

Major Hanson, he directed, was to take B company up the Haddington Road and secure Baggot Street bridge. He was then to advance westwards along the *southern* side of the canal . . . along Percy Place . . . and take the schools in flank.

Due to the confusion of the battle, and the nature of the intelligence report, the military still had no idea that the fire directed at them came from the northern side of the bridge, and that, when advancing on the schools via the canal bank,

105

they would completely expose their flank to the rebels in Clanwilliam House, across the water.

Hanson ordered his company forward at the double—rounding Number 25 while Fane's men provided covering fire. But Grace and Malone were too securely barricaded to care very much about the British bullets, and B Company, too, was mauled before starting on the march that was to outflank Reynolds' defences.

* * *

In view of the fact that Reynolds and his men had been positioned for at least forty-eight hours in a middle-class and conservative district where probably as many as ninety percent of the residents hated the Sinn Fein movement and everything it stood for, and were only too anxious to co-operate with the forces of the Crown, the glaring inaccuracy of the intelligence report, which so tragically misled even such an experienced fighting soldier as Fane and led to the bloodiest battle in the history of the rebellion, remains to this day a tantalising mystery. But almost equally strange, in retrospect, is the lack of appreciation shown by the usually shrewd de Valera of the importance of the Mount Street bridge position, only 200 yards to his right, and his failure to reinforce it.

While the sound of battle raged in Northumberland Road, the future President's main force—occupying Boland's Mill, spread along the railway line, and masking Beggar's Bush Barracks—remained inactive. It waited on the defensive, for an attack against its front. Pleas for support from Reynolds were met with the retort that there were no men to spare. Rations were despatched, but no extra ammunition. In Clanwilliam House, Roberts Yard, the Parochial Hall, and Number 25, the defenders of Mount Street Bridge were left to fend for themselves. Thus despite his initial success—expressed in the deadly toll he had exacted among the Sherwoods—it was perhaps with a note of despair that Reynolds now addressed his little band on the necessity to "hold" against the fresh attacks that he could see were imminent. Every hour they could delay the British advance was an hour gained for their comrades in the provinces—*that* myth wasn't quite dead yet!—to reach the city and take part in the fight. Besides all were conversant with the latest exciting news to come from the propagandists of the Post Office: the Germans were about to march into the suburbs! Had Reynolds but known it, the possibility of a German intervention was also present in the mind of Colonel Fane . . .

* * *

"Had he (Fane) shrunk from the issue he adopted," writes the 2/7th's historian, "the rebellion would have been more protracted . . . Colonel Fane knew that, though not fighting Germans, he was fighting Germany."

It is in the context of this observation that much of the wasteful valour that characterised the Battle of Mount Street Bridge, and much of the ferocity of the subsequent fighting in north east Dublin can be explained. To H.Q. speed was the essence in suppressing the rebellion. They could not believe that its authors would have taken so desperate a plunge without being assured in advance of German support, or that, even if they had, the Germans could be so dull as not to capitalise on it. Again, despite the efficiency of the R.I.C. and the widespread arrests in the countryside that had followed the outbreak in Dublin, fears of a general rising still persisted, and had indeed been greatly aggravated by news that came from two counties as far apart as Wexford and Galway.

Looking back, there are elements in the Galway confrontation that smack of the medieval, or almost the absurd. Four hundred rebels had been reported on the march, and—to quote a contemporary account—"apprehensions had been entertained" that they would seize Merlin Park, "the residence of Captain and Lady Philippa Wauthorpe." To prevent this happening, it is gratifying to record, the local gentry armed themselves, and, some of them on horseback, put themselves at the head of their tenantry, equipped with shotguns and pikes: the police meanwhile preparing to resist an attack on the town itself. It was the Navy's intervention, however, that finally scotched the rebel offensive. A destroyer appeared offshore, and, to quote yet once more "the big guns rang out in the bay, and Galway was saved!"

In Wexford, the local Volunteer leader, Robert Brennan —backed by two newspapermen, Laurence de Lacy and J. R. Etchingham—provided an isolated example of the aid the sorely-pressed Dublin Brigade so desperately needed. In the historic old town of Enniscorthy—hallowed by its memories of the rising of '98—the rebels rose to delay British reinforcements, approaching Dublin from Rosslare. They seized the railway station, and held up a train carrying 300 workmen to Kynoch's, the munition works in Arklow, in neighbouring County Wicklow. They then considered destroying Enniscorthy's ancient bridge, but mercifully had second thoughts and attempted instead to blow up the bridge of Scarawalsh, crossing the river Slaney on the main road to Wexford. They then captured the little town of Ferns—much to its residents' bewilderment—and were now said to be advancing reinforced on Gorey.

One other rebel force was known to be in the field: a small but well-armed group handled skilfully by Richard Mulcahy and Thomas Ashe in North County Dublin. There were also reports of a projected rebel plan to seize the Marconi Wireless Station on the Skerries.

Following the initial agreement that calm prevailed in all areas outside the capital itself, these disturbances achieved in the eyes of the authorities an importance that, although now seen to have been exaggerated, looked very differently in the context of the time.

Speed in suppression was the essence . . .

* * *

Re-grouping after their losses from Number 25, Hanson's men continued their advance along the Haddington Road and reached Baggot Street bridge.

With his ears still ringing to the echo of the rifles and automatics in Northumberland Road Hanson needed no prodding as to the urgency of his mission. He hurriedly despatched a platoon to secure the bridge itself, and then turned right—to lead his men in single file along the canal bank towards the schools. In Clanwilliam House, over the water, the rebels watched the move in a sort of reverential stupefaction. "What the hell," was the attitude, "do they think they're doing now?"

Reynolds' men were not alone in their wonderment. A few minutes earlier—in Number 25—Grace and Malone had been similarly affected when suddenly, after fierce covering fire, a group of Sherwoods, cheering wildly had dashed past them, and up the street, with seeming disregard for loss; until finally chopped down by the men in the Parochial Hall.

Ignorant of the intelligence report—and the way in which it had misled their opponents as to the main point of resistance—the rebels regarded the English movements as those of madmen, bent on suicide.

Reynolds waited until Hanson's men, continuing to press on towards the Schools, had almost reached the corner of the bridge, and thus could be commanded from both the front, side and back windows of his fortress. Then sharply he ordered: "Rapid fire!"

To Hanson, the pinhead flashes that lit the dark windows of the house across the still canal came as a revelation. Next

second, he was reeling wounded across the embankment, and
yelling to his men to take shelter behind its low brick wall.
So *this* was what had gone wrong with the attack up Northumberland Road! Even now though, he did not realise that
the school itself was not held. He went down behind the wall,
his company crouched behind him, while he tried to resolve
how to fulfil a twofold role: silence the riflemen in
Clanwilliam House in order to reach his objective.

* * *

While waiting for Hanson to work round via the Baggot
Bridge flank, Fane arranged for an attempt to be made to get
at the rebels from the east. A force of the 2/7th attempted to
infiltrate up Canal Street, but was met by the fire of de
Valera's outposts—still positioned to resist attack from
Beggar's Bush Barracks—and forced back.

Bitterly cursing the fools who had deprived his battalion
of its machine-guns and grenades, Fane now sent back to
headquarters an S.O.S. for both. *Speed* was the essence . . .

MacConochey, back at Ballsbridge and chafing at the delay
to his right-hand column—the left had proceeded along the
Stillorgan-Donnybrook road almost completely unopposed—
called Oates, and asked for the 2/8th to lend a hand, by
sending a flanking force to assist the 2/7th on their right.
He was astounded when Lowe brusquely countermanded the
order. The Sherwoods must press frontally, and push on "at
all costs."

Not happy at the suggestion, the Brigadier called for his
horse and went to see for himself just what was holding up
the attack. Shocked at the 2/7th's casualty list, he went
speedily back again, and once more got on the telephone to
Lowe. The latter was impatient.

MacConochey explained the setup. The 2/7th were terribly
cut up, and Fane was wounded. Was the attack on Mount
Street Bridge so vital after all? At Baggot Street Bridge there
was no resistance at all . . .

Lowe, still irritable, repeated his earlier edict. The School
must be taken, "at all costs." Frustratedly MacConochey
turned to Oates, and ordered the 2/8th up to the attack.

."Your battalion will storm the Mount Street Schools at all
costs . . . *at all costs mind*, and penetrate further if you can."

* * *

Back in O'Connell Street, a deep-voiced rebel started to
sing the mournful refrain of "Wrap the Green Flag Round

Me." His comrades joined in, while the field guns—as if by way of cynical parenthesis—again began to shoot. In Dublin Castle, Dr W. K. Carew, the medical superintendent, began to cope with yet another batch of casualties, washed up in the wake of the fighting in the city centre. The doctor had not changed his clothes since he rose on Monday morning. He would still not have changed them by Saturday night. In Kingstown, young Harry Bate had only one thin slice of toast for tea—bread was short, and there were cakes or biscuits. It was, he gathered, the fault of the bad men . . . the bad men the soldiers were now fighting in the city . . . the bad men who were responsible for the curfew. Not a shot had been fired in Kingstown since the start of the rising: but people were forbidden to be on the streets between 7.30 at night and 5.30 in the morning. Meanwhile, for Mrs Spellman over on North Side it was a time for goodbyes and sadness.

It was just after noon when the first British patrols had begun to move into the neighbourhood. Now the hour had come for her soldier guests to leave. "We'll remember you, Ma," said the boy with the London accent. The Irishman hugged her tight. "Sure, we'll meet you in happier times." Before they left, they wrote their names and addresses in her diary, and composed for good measure a little note to say how well she had looked after them. This they signed with the respective names of their respective units, and added to their own names their regimental numbers.

"But you needn't have written all this," she said, a little bewildered. "I'm not trying to advertise for lodgers. . . ."

"Might come in handy, Ma," the Londoner answered awkwardly. "You never know . . . after all this fighting . . . our lads might play a bit rough."

Mrs Spellman never saw "her" soldiers again. For a while, she got letters from the Londoner: the last one was written just before the Somme retreat. The parents of the Irishman paid her a visit: he had been killed in Mesopotamia. But the note of warning struck by the pair as they'd prepared their testimonial turned out to be fully justified. Rough indeed were to be methods of some of the English troops, fresh from the fury of the battle.

At the moment however, these things were in the future. On her own . . . hungry . . . and listening to the gunfire roll across the city . . . she burst into tears of loneliness and grief.

CHAPTER TEN

Tears, too, there were near Lower Mount Street for the boys of the 2/7th . . . tears from the residents of Northumberland Road and Percy Place, and the rebel-held side of the dark strip of water on which had been lavished so extravagant an expenditure of futile bravery and blood.

Desperately, tenaciously, with backs bowed beneath the weight of their full packs, and with rifles clutched by hands that sweated, the young soldiers came on. They came to order, as if on exercise, and each time each wave was sent recoiling backwards, split into eddies by the fire from Clanwilliam House. They came to the whistle blast—theirs not to reason why—and they came until the bridge and its approaches were pockmarked by their fallen.

By this time, Reynolds' men in the House were themselves under fire. The flashes that had brought to Hanson belated realisation of the source of the "oblique" fire had also been spotted by the marksmen he had installed near Baggot Street Bridge. Their reactions were sharp.

At first the British bullets had a solely nuisance value. Soon they were hosing the house in their thousands; machine-gun support had at last arrived. They burrowed through the chinks between the barricades of furniture that blocked the tall sash-windows. They ricochetted wildly from wall to wall. They dissolved the chandelier in a shower of crystal splinters. Soon, to cross from one side of the drawing-room to another necessitated a journey on all fours. As the weight of the fire literally ate away their timber defences, the rebels were forced to press themselves against the stone piers. Yet still they continued to shoot, until their rifles burned their hands, threatened to explode in their faces, and were cooled in the water that ran from the punctured pipes.

Once more the Sherwoods attacked, and once more the Mausers and Martinis flashed sparks from the stone of the bridge, swept the charging men from their feet, and hit—again and again—the wounded who piled the hump from the charge before. A sort of disgust set in among the rebels at the toll exacted by their own success: they fired mechanically and coldbloodedly but they no longer fired with relish. And then—at this stage of the battle—a wild impulse overcame those whose role was but to look on. As if moved by a common reaction against the slaughter, the local people risked their lives to end it.

"Cease fire!"

Reynolds had shouted the self-same order an hour or so before, when white sheets had been waved from the windows of the houses lining the far side of the canal, and people regardless of degree—maid servants and residents and the man from the shop on the corner—had dashed out on to the bridge to carry the wounded to shelter. But now the pressure for mercy came from an additional quarter; from a crowd that had collected to the rebel garrison's rear.

"Cease fire!" he repeated.

In the British lines too a silence fell, as the tired soldiers watched what one of them recalls as "the most moving moment I've lived through."

Two young girls led the advance on to the bridge. One of them was 17-year-old Louise Nolan. She was carrying a large enamel jug, filled with water for the wounded. With Louise was her sister, and, close behind them came a clergyman, other local residents, a group of red cross nurses, and two doctors from a nearby hospital. As they came up to the house one of the latter stopped, to ask permission to pass.

Reynolds shrugged impatiently "Okay, get on with it."

For several minutes the uncanny quiet persisted while the strangely assorted crowd busied itself on its mission of mercy: and then, once more, Reynolds had to yell his men to action, and bullets snarled both ways across the bridge.

*　　*　　*

It was just after 4.30 when—at the far end of the road—the battle switched decisively against the rebels. The bombs that Fane had asked for had at last arrived, and, with them, the debonair Captain Jeffaires, a bombing instructor from the Dublin garrison.

Once more the 2/7th went into the assault, and, on the third charge, the tommies managed to reach the lee of Number 25. But this time there was no repetition of the events that had caused their previous attacks to end in stalemate. No longer did bayonets stab—frantically and futilely—the tight-locked chairs and tables that blocked the windows or shoulders hopelessly heave against the reinforced front door. Instead, while the rifles of their friends searched the face of the building, Corporal H. Hutchinson and Pte J. F. Booth of the Battalion Bombing Section—narrowly missed by a burst from Malone's automatic—ran up the short front path, slammed gun cotton on the massive door handle, flattened themselves on the ground and waited . . .

The explosion that blew the door down was followed by others: the explosions of hand grenades hurled by Jeffaires' team. And then, with a cheer, half a dozen of the men stormed across the front garden, and vanished into the billowing dust and smoke and debris of the hall.

A minute or so later, a rifle was jabbed through a window, and waggled triumphantly at the Sherwood riflemen in the houses opposite. On the tip of its blood-stained bayonet was impaled a rebel hat.

The incredible defence was over.

* * *

"At all costs. . . ."

With Number 25 silenced, Oates's 2/8th moved from the side-street—St Mary's Road—where they had waited so impatiently since Fane's initial repulse, and under the eye of the C.O. and Maconochie, moved to assault the next objective: the Parochial Halls.

Immediately they suffered casualties, but stormed on. And this time the resistance of the rebels cracked: cracked at the sight of the khaki mass that hurled itself towards them. To the tiny garrison, there seemed to be no end or limit to the British resources. The men fled to the rear of the Halls, then into the lane beyond. And there, overtaken, they were speedily cut down.

Flushed with triumph, "A" and "B" companies now moved on towards the school, but once more the fire from Clanwilliam House exacted its deadly toll.

It was to a young platoon commander—Lieutenant Hunter—that there fell the distinction of taking the objective that had led to so costly an expenditure of effort and blood.

While the remnants of the first attack waves, grabbing what cover they could in the front gardens of Northumberland Road, and extending their flanks through the houses of Percy Place dropped a blanket of fire on the School and Clanwilliam House, Foster led an assault party to storm the School itself.

Conspicuously the main target of the fire from over the bridge, with bullets zipping around his shoulders so closely as to scorch the pips on his tunic, he hurled himself almost blindly at the iron railings surrounding the school, desperately hauled himself up. For a fraction of a second he squatted awkwardly on the iron spikes, expecting any moment a bullet in back or stomach, and then dropped into the grounds beyond, drawing and firing his revolver as he did so. With the sort of despairing loyalty that was a characteristic of both sides on this day, his men came too.

To their astonishment, they were met with no searing blast of rebel fire. They kicked open the main door, stood aside and entered the classrooms. Not a shot was fired. The only occupants of the school were the caretaker and his wife. Both were dead. Chopped down by the crossfire of a battle in which neither had played a part, except as victims.

*　　*　　*

For the garrison at Clanwilliam the end was now in sight. The School in their possession, and the houses in Percy Place, the British now fanned out to left and right along the canal banks, to bring down a crossfire of such intensity that the house literally trembled to the smack of bullets. The stucco of the front flew like hail. Inside the drawing room, men moved in a haze of dust from the dislodged plaster from the ceilings. Curtains and carpets smouldered. A small fire had to be stamped out. Yet still Reynolds scorned all thought of retreat. A sort of ecstasy would appear to have held the rebels at this stage, despite the sure knowledge that their efforts could have only one sort of ending. They had halted the repeated—and never-failingly courageous—attacks of an enemy who, however much misled by his own intelligence service, and however much handicapped by the fact that he could not deploy his strength in full, outnumbered them by nearly sixty to one. They had held up the advance of the right wing of the British force for five hours or more: they were still holding it. It was unfortunate—from their point of view—that no attempt was made to profit by the bonus their courage had won. McDonagh, in the Robert's Yard position, had again appealed to de Valera to send reinforcements from Boland's Mill. And again those reinforcements were refused him.

*　　*　　*

Back at the Post Office it was fairly plain that whatever else the rebel leadership lacked it certainly was not colour. Plunkett, during the brief periods when his devouring illness ceased to bite, appeared with ear-rings dangling from beneath his officer's hat, a single spur trailing cowboy-style from his hand-tooled riding boots, a naked sabre hanging at his side. Tom Clarke—the old Fenian—adjusted his pince nez, jiggled his adam's apple in excitement, and helped himself to a rifle when a brief rumour spread of an "imminent" attack from British patrols, sighted in the North-west area. Connolly whose energy appeared to be inexhaustible, beamed down upon the bullet-swept pavements, repeated again and again his constant refrain of "we're winning", and gave forecasts —tipster style—of the time when the Germans would break through on the Maas road. But probably the most interesting of all the rebel leaders was their president, Padraic Pearse. Tall, slightly stooping, the wide eyes in the fine head burning with sleeplessness and a sort of unquenchable passion he moved like a man elated—by thoughts of martyrdom, perhaps?—among the little army that had turned his dreams into history.

Long ago he had foreseen this hour. Foreseen it with no illusions about its possible aftermath. His second communique, just completed, was as full of optimism as its predecessor: yet already, he must have felt, the time of reckoning was approaching. In 1914, when the Brotherhood had made its momentous decision—for armed insurrection, with German aid if possible—he had confided to his dearly loved Mother, "We will all be killed." In his poetry, he reflected—like his fellow poet and comrade Thomas MacDonagh—time after time again his appreciation of his ultimate destiny. But like the English idealist Rupert Brooke he could look to that destiny almost as a man looks to his mistress. Flushed with love he was ready for the ultimate embrace.

For by now it was abundantly plain that as a military operation designed to attain immediate success, the rising had failed. Communications with even the southern end of the city itself were almost completely cut. News came sketchily, long overdue, and mostly by word of mouth from scouts who had to run a gauntlet of British fire. From the provinces there came no news at all. The men who laboured to erect a wireless transmitter on the dome of the Dublin Bread Company had at last begun to transmit the fact of the rising to the world. But there was no indication at all that their message had been heard. Yet still, incredibly, the morale of rank and file stayed high. Copies of the proclamation of martial law had somehow found their way into the strong-hold; but they cut no ice with the heads-in-the-clouds Volunteers. Nor did the lack of professionalism shown by the rebel leadership in incurring its current series of reverses register upon the majority of the headquarters group. To be fair, it should be added on this score that the "professionals"

115

themselves sometimes cut a rather disappointing figure.

* * *

"Led by their Colonel, they went forward with a spirit and dash that showed they were fit to take their place beside the finest troops in the army . . ." such was the way in which Maconochie was to write of the sacrifice shown by the gallant 2/8th. He did not mention that that sacrifice would have been unnecessary, were it not for the insistence of Command. Why was it so important for the Sherwoods to storm Lower Mount Street frontally? Why couldn't they have launched—as he and Oates and Fane had so ardently desired—enveloping moves from the bridges to east and west? Maconochie did not press for an answer: or, if he did, he failed to make it public.

The Brigadier, the two Colonels, the junior officers: they had done all that it was possible to do—possible within the limits of what today may seem to have an extraordinary directive—when the time came for the 2/8th to take over from Fane's mauled battalion.

To mitigate the effects of that directive they had managed —though not at the first asking—to procure machine-guns, to replace the ones they had been forced to leave behind in Liverpool, and mounted them at tactical points along the canal bank to step-up covering fire. They had managed— eventually—to get the bombs that were so desperately needed . . . the bombs they had been forbidden to take with them when they had embarked. But, in the meanwhile, they had suffered losses that were treble—or more—the losses they might have been, had the guns and bombs been available from the start. And the "all costs" emphasis had been heavily re-emphasised . . . re-emphasised all the way down the line. Like it—and they didn't—lump it—and they did—the troops were still doomed to essay the route that led them through the bottleneck of the bridge. They were still confined, at point blank range, to operate in a space where their very numbers handicapped rather than helped.

The first attack of the 2/8th withered away like that of the 2/7th. And, like their sore-tried sister unit, the 2/8th tried again.

"A" and "B" companies being halted, "C" was called forward. The Battalion Adjutant—Captain Leslie Melville —went with them "for the trip." He was the first to fall. Others fell too. Short of the bridge, "C" Company was called to a bloodied halt.

Once more there was the briefest of brief lulls in the firing. And once more the Nolans, joined, on this occasion, by army nurses from the British side of the canal, dashed out to do their work of salving the human debris that remained. This was only a quarter done when a flurry of shots announced the resumption of the tragedy.

* * *

Between the canal bank and the rear of the school an advertising hoarding blocked the line of vision of both Reynolds' force and O'Donaghue's section, still installed in Robert's Yard. Behind this obstacle, Captain Quibbell of "B" re-grouped a scratch force drawn from all three companies, and planned yet another assault.

From where he crouched, Quibbell could catch—though intermittently—brief glimpses of Oates, down in Northumberland Road, egging-on selected marksmen into the front gardens of the tall mansions to give him covering-fire. Opposite him, over to the western side of the bridge approach, squatted a young subaltern—Lt Elliott—and two men: all that was left of what had been a full-strength platoon. Between Elliott and him three khaki mounds stirred and groaned, and cried un-nervingly for water. And three other mounds lay bloody and very still.

Such was the daunting scene on which Quibbell gazed as he braced himself for the word that he must give. He could see nothing of the rebel side of the canal. He couldn't lift his head over the low stone wall because of the bullets that ripped and tore their way through the hoarding. He aimed to dash around the eastern corner of the bridge, while Elliott and his men—all two of them—attacked from the western side.

And then IT came, the signal that was his cue; the fierce opening of the orchestra of rifles and machine-guns. "Forward!" he yelled.

Quibbell, slightly hunched, dashed from the shelter of the parapet and up the slight slope to the hump of the bridge. Behind him came Captain Cursham, of "B" Company, a few survivors of the 2/8th, and the indefatigable Foster, still cock-a-hoop after his "capture" of the school. Elliott joined in the rush, the two privates gamely following. And once more they saw the House and its tall windows become alive with darting pinheads of light. The attack faltered. The attackers went down among the wounded and the dead. Then Quibbell, in a momentary lull, once more screamed to his shattered troop to charge. This time they reached their objective, or

117

rather a point that was in bombing distance of it. The front of the House was wracked by a series of explosions.

*   *   *

There was no anti-climax about the fall of Clanwilliam House. To the last it maintained its daunting reputation. Quibbell was wounded. Cursham took command. Cursham was wounded, and died a little later. Foster maintained the attack, until Quibbell recovered. It was a battle fought at point-blank range. No quarter was asked or given. The rebels threw down their rifles, and hosed their attackers with revolver bullets. The soldiers got to within touching-distance of the wall. And then the attack force found itself short of bombs.

"I'll get some more," the voice was Elliott's.

"Pluckily" as Colonel Oates was later to put it—with a soldier's flair for understatement—he recrossed the bridge, and came back again with the grenades, heaped casually in a bucket.

*   *   *

It was not until the British were breaking down the door that Reynolds decided to give the word to quit. He had scarcely uttered the command when a stray bullet hit him. One of his men crawled over to him, with a pannikin of water. Two others whispered the Act of Contrition in his ear. Then, all was over.

The three survivors made their way to the back entrance just as Foster came in from the front. A figure swayed towards him out of the gloom. He shot him, then ran his bayonet through him—just to make sure. He saw two other men, crouched by the window. So he rolled a grenade between them, then slammed the door behind him. A tongue of flame roared upward to the ceiling and, justly considering he had done his stint and more, the young Lieutenant reeled back into the open air.

CHAPTER ELEVEN

As the ambulances brought the Sherwoods dead and wounded back to the spot from which they had so light-heartedly taken their first look at Ireland, scarcely twelve hours before, and the flames from Clanwilliam House marked the funeral pyre of Reynolds and his men, the military inside the city itself had not been slow to add to the tally of incidents that marked Wednesday as the point of no return for those who still hoped, against all reason, for some form of accommodation and settlement.

With the Castle secure—and Nathan being hailed by the press, though not for long, as the brains behind its defence —a strong force of the Leinsters, brought in with Lowe's 24th Brigade, succeeded in relieving the O.T.C. at Trinity, and then deployed along the South bank of the river, opening fire on O'Connell Street.

Meanwhile, another detachment of the Crown Forces, from the Curragh, at last began to seriously menace the rebel defences of the city to the north-west.

Way for this move had been prepared by an attack on the barricades thrown up by Daly's men to guard their right flank against a move from Broadstone Station, which they had not the resources to occupy. The defences and the rebels manning them were swept aside in a matter of minutes, and it wasn't long before Connolly got to hear of the reason why. The British were doing what he had said they would never do. They were using artillery.

It was perhaps appropriate that the gun that fired the first shell should have been positioned in the local lunatic asylum . . .

By the afternoon, Daly also found himself in trouble to his front, formed by the northern quaysides, of which the Four Courts was at once the citadel and prize.

Unopposed—though *why* unopposed is yet another of the rising's enigmas—fields guns had arrived at Trinity. Now their barrels were trained across the Liffey—aimed at the Mendicity Institution, a strongpoint on the Four Courts flank.

At 2.40 they opened fire.

The rebels who, until now, had staged a heroic resistance

to all attempts to dislodge them, stumbled out dazedly a half
hour later: their hands held high.

* * *

One way or the other it was not Daly's day. Even the
barracks he had captured from the Pay Corps was destined to
be a thorn in his side.

Certainly one of the most competent of the rebel
commanders, this tough Dubliner was one of the worst hit
victims of the leadership's lack of military expertise. The
Command's insistence on sticking to the original defence plan
for the city—even though the premise on which that plan had
been approved, namely a full turnout, had been killed by the
confusion of the Countermanding Order—had placed Daly in
an impossible position.

With less than 300 men at his disposal, Daly was supposed
to defend not only the Four Courts and the quays. He was
also expected to hold British attempts to infiltrate through the
city's western suburbs, occupy Broadstone Station, and harry
units attempting to advance from Phoenix Park. It was a
situation that would have made a lesser man throw in his
hand.

The problem of what to do about the Linenhall Barracks
was typical of the commandant's many headaches. With his
men so thin on the ground, he decided he could not afford to
take possession. On the other hand, he could not leave the
place a vacuum, to be filled in by the military patrols, react-
ing ever more aggressively as Lowe's plans to isolate the
respective rebel groups increased momentum. Reluctantly, he
decided to set the place ablaze. Unfortunately, his men did
the job with too much enthusiasm.

They stacked the barracks with drums of oil, but hopelessly
underestimated its incendiary effect. Within seconds the flames
had leapt across the street. They caught a shop, enveloped a
barricade, and spread to—of all things—a chemical factory.
Soon the blaze was completely uncontrollable, scorching and
driving back the Volunteers for scores of yard. And then,
from the heart of the inferno came a series of explosions,
carrying its destructive power still further. Soon it could be
seen for miles away, and from both sides—and the hapless
civilians caught between them—the sight brought recrimina-
tion, and horrified alarm.

To Captain Knight, still with the imperial forces in Phoenix
Park, the smoke pillar in the sky was a sign that the rebels
had turned desperate, or drunk, or—even more likely—were

demonstrating their bloody-minded joy in sheer destruction. The "gangsters" were resorting to arson.

Among the defenders of Jacobs' the story was that the British were to blame: Lowe's troops had turned Cromwellian, and were burning everything in their path. Even the veteran MacBride—able to draw on his first-hand experiences of the Boer War—drew false inferences from the position of the outbreak.

Already cottoning-on to the general motive behind the apparently disconnected movements of the Crown units inside the city, MacBride felt that the blaze signified that the British were now duplicating Lowe's southern axis on the north side of the river. There was no faltering, however, in the spirit of the Jacobs' defenders. No weakening in their resolve to soldier-on. Already they had broken up repeated bayonet charges. Grimly they braced themselves for a tougher fight to come.

*　　*　　*

There were men by their hundreds inside the Castle now. From being beleagured it had become, in a matter of hours, the hub of all military activity south of the river. Castle Yard threw back the echoes of shouted commands, the oaths of troopers, the clatter of hooves, and the rumble of the steel-rimmed wheels of guns and wagons. No longer blacked-out for fear of rebel snipers, the barrack square was lit by enormous watchfires, around which the men of the Leinsters stamped and jostled, warming themselves by the blaze. The red glow was reflected on the bayonets of the stacked rifles, forming neat pyramids of threes, while from the darkness that reigned at the top of the Bermingham Tower came the occasional tearing echo of rifle shots. Ammunition boxes clattered on to the cobbles. Artillery limbers creaked past to Trinity. The Castle was now short of two things only: food, the men were rationed to half a slice of bread three times a day, and the facilities for formal military funerals.

The V.A.D. saw 70 burials that night, in the graves she'd seen dug in the morning.

She helped sew the dead in sheets: the castle had run out of coffins . . .

Death featured largely too in the mind of Colonel Oates. The 2/8th had lost eighteen dead, two of them officers, personal friends. Six officers and sixty-three other ranks had been wounded. The 2/7th had been even harder hit: three officers and fifteen other ranks killed; eight officers and sixty-five other ranks wounded. In all, the Battle of Mount Street Bridge had cost the territorials 171 casualties, 36 of them fatal. Considering the gain, Oates reflected, the price had been high.

Withdrawn to Ballsbridge, where the Horticultural Hall was pressed into service as a temporary H.Q., the Sherwoods had been joined by the company they had left behind at Liverpool. Among their officers was Oates's son, disappointed at missing the "scrap." As a soldier, the Colonel sympathised. As a father, his feelings were different.

Now, having gone the rounds among his young soldiers, of whose gallantry and perseverance under fire he was justly proud, Oates returned to the two subjects that, for years to come, were to vex and perplex him, and other survivors too. First, was the refusal of the port authorities to let the battalion embark its Lewis guns. Of this, he was to write with bitterness, "The value of the presence of even two of these guns would have been incalculable. The British army seems fated to have its work blocked or rendered as difficult as possible by officials trusted with a little brief authority, whose orders must not be questioned, and who rarely have to answer for results."

The other thing that bothered Oates was the directive he had received from the Brigadier. "Your battalion will storm the Mount Street Schools at all costs . . . *at all costs, mind!*" Well, the Sherwoods had done just that: but had it been really necessary? Just *why* the insistence on the attack through Mount Street? After the terrible mauling received by Fane, just why weren't the two battalions allowed to cross by Baggot Street Bridge? Where their comrades had advanced with such little opposition? Oates was to puzzle over such questions until his dying day: but he never got a really satisfactory answer.

However, on the night of Wednesday 26th, this form of speculation had to be temporarily curtailed. After sleep, Oates was informed, the Sherwoods would be on the move again. There was work for them to do, "at all costs. . . ."

*   *   *

While the Sherwood Foresters snatched their rest, and the South Staffs pressed on towards the northwest, to battle with Kent's group, in the labyrinth of the South Dublin Union, there was tough fighting for the Irish regiments to their north, where the triangular shaped bulk of Jacobs' factory, rearing six storeys high, formed the sole remaining rebel stronghold in the centre, dominating Portobello Bridge, and the roads leading to the Castle.

After their initial underestimate of their opponents' fighting capacity, the military had learned their lesson. Courage and dash was not enough to crack the amateurs; the "cornerboys" must be treated with respect.

Jacobs' was now under concentrated fire, and the soldiers were showing ingenuity as well as professional skill. They had requisitioned a batch of steam-engine boilers, driven loopholes through them and mounted them on trucks to use as a form of armoured car. The sight of these monsters had demoralised rebel pickets—whose bullets did little more than flash sparks from their iron sides—and a follow-up force of infantry had been able to seize St Patrick's Park, just opposite the factory. Snipers on Jacobs' roof had been able to flush them out, but elsewhere the British attacks were pressed home with quick success, driving the outposts back on to McDonagh's main position.

True that, even now, certain of the imperial officers retained sufficient contempt for the "amateurs" to lapse into tactical blunders. An attempt was made to plant heavy machine-guns in the middle of Digges Street—guns and gunners were blasted away by the Howth mausers of the defenders. Again, although the tenements in Bride Street afforded excellent cover close to the rear of the factory no attempt was made to occupy them. But otherwise, there was a marked difference in mood and method among the attackers since the costly attacks of the morning. The tommies no longer advanced in the open street. Instead they were methodically pickaxing their route through the walls of the terraced buildings, edging their way forward literally inch by inch.

There was a marked increase in artillery fire. Although the shells were not aimed at the factory, but at the positions north of the river, the crunch of their distant explosions acted as a perpetual reminder to the rebels of the sort of odds they might presently be expected to face. The sky seemed to open and shut with the flashes of the guns, and then be spread with the stain of a dozen fires.

> "We'll sing a song, a soldier's song
>   With cheering, rousing chorus
> As round our blazing fires we throng,
>   The starry heavens o'er us;
> Impatient for the coming fight,
>   And as we wait the morning's light
> Here in the silence of the night
>   We'll chant a soldier's song . . ."

To Patrick Kearney, as author, the stirring words might

normally have seemed to be particularly apposite to this night of flames and battle. But, at the time, he was far too tired to care. Except for the odd cat-nap, he and his section had had no rest for the past seventy hours or more: a fact that Authority had only recently appreciated.

It was with intense gratitude that they now allowed themselves to be led to the bunks and palliasses of the sleeping quarters that had been improvised in the very heart of the factory, and, still clutching their rifles, prepared to make the most of it . . .

* * *

"You, and you . . . get up and follow me!"

They had hardly started to nod when the officer aroused them. They glared at him through bleary eyes, in resentment and disgust.

"At the double," he said . . .

Hell, why pick on them?

The women's detachment, penned up in the College of Surgeons, was desperately short of food and Jacobs' had been ordered to send in a ration party. Kearney's group had been "specially selected" for the job: only the best was good enough. Unimpressed by the compliment, the Volunteers felt the choice unfair. Last men to be given a chance to rest, they had occupied outside positions on the long row of palliasses, and had happened to be easy to reach. However, as Kearney eventually philosophised, it would be nice to have a little feminine company.

* * *

The trip itself was an unenviable experience. The Volunteers had to dash from turning to turning, without any clear idea as to which one might bring them head on to the enemy. Although there was no street lighting, parts of the route were as bright as day in the glare from the burning buildings, playing tricks with the shadows of the hurrying men. Over from the Liffey a searchlight wavered indeterminately, flickering from sky to waterfront. At the crackling explosion of a flare, men jumped to fears hitherto unknown.

Despite the fierce assaults of the Crown Forces there was still a route held open to the College, but machine-guns commanded most of the road crossings, and snipers were believed to be prowling the roof-tops.

That, considering these circumstances, the party managed to reach its objective at all—let alone reach it without a single casualty—was a cause for wonderment as well as thanksgiving among the Volunteers. And equally wonderful did they find the appearance of the ladies they'd delivered from the pressing threat of famine. Among them all, though, the Countess reigned supreme: sartorially as well as socially a rebel par excellence. A Sam Brown spanned the smooth texture of her uniform jacket—made to a pattern that she had herself designed. She carried in gleaming holster a Mauser machine-pistol. But what particularly caught the rebel-poet's eye was her nice line in satin breeches.

For years to come Kearney was to treasure the memory of this redoubtable amazon. Moving among her less elegant sisters with the poise of a hostess at a Parisian salon, she received the ration party with an air that put fire into their bellies, and sent them back to Jacobs' in a mood of devil-may-care arrogance, fortified and sustained by the applause that the brave receive from the fair. It was regrettable that, on their return, there should have to be a deflating anti-climax . . .

The College had had a well-stocked armoury, for an O.T.C. that, unlike that of Trinity, had not had the chance to organise and fight. And Mallin had yielded to the fatigue party part of his capture, good Lee-Enfield rifles, together with ammunition. But no sooner had the redoubtable Commandant Hunter welcomed the volunteers back, and praised them for the good work and the useful "loot", than he asked: "But where are the bayonets?"

Bayonets!

Hopelessly, the men looked to one another. "We didn't think of the bayonets . . ."

"Then," said Hunter briskly, "you had better go back and get them!"

By the time that Kearney and his friends once more returned to Jacobs', it was too late to think of sleep. Time now to stand-to—and face yet another attack from the persistent British.

"When," they asked despairingly, "will we be reinforced from the country?"

* * *

Back in London, popular fury against the insurgents—"paid for by German gold" was the description that really damned them—had reached gale force. Husbands, sons and loved ones—all had been vilely betrayed: stabbed in the back by a pack of scheming traitors. Within forty-eight hours public

125

feeling rose to boiling-point, and Whitehall fears of adverse reaction to "toughness" had been replaced by near panic at the consequences of being considered too soft.

Ominously, Carson went on record in the House as hoping that no section of the newspapers would try "during a war of such a character as we are in", to bring about "a discussion of a political concern", in relation to the Irish question. The Ulster leader need not have worried. He had scarcely finished his speech before John Redmond had risen to express "the overwhelming feeling of horror and dismay" with which he and his colleagues regarded what they called "these proceedings" in Dublin: while, on the same day, the Daily Mirror's gossip columnist, "The Rambler", had confined his remarks to recording—though perhaps rather naively—"I found my Irish journalistic colleagues in the Irish nationalist press particularly pleased about Sir Roger's capture."

Even news-wise, the rebellion did not always enjoy the dignity of a lead story. While the Castle was being relieved, and Lowe was sending in his artillery to exploit the column's success, the Mirror was giving greater prominence to the news that "five hun gasbags" had dropped bombs on the Eastern Counties, and "inflicted severe injuries" to the arm of a London stockbroker who had incautiously looked out of the window of his country retreat. England too had her Home Front tribulations.

But whatever the degree of emphasis placed on the rising by the press, everywhere the question was being asked—and asked with increasing acerbity—"why hadn't anyone *known?*" In the Cabinet, the Army, the Civil Service, hurt feelings were soon to explode in recriminations of a bitterness hitherto unparalleled. Meanwhile, however, an uneasy unity prevailed though only in one respect. The military must get the matter over with—and get it over with fast. In justice to the soldiers, it should be said they were attempting to do just that . . .

* * *

On Thursday the 27th the unfortunate General Friend was relieved of his command, and replaced by General Sir John Maxwell, a fighting solder of the Kitchener school.

Maxwell knew little about Ireland, but a lot about Egypt. Unfairly, he was to gain the sobriquet of Butcher.

CHAPTER TWELVE

Less than three weeks before the events in Dublin that were to give him, on the one hand, a reputation for decisive military action and, on the other, the sanguinary tag that was to endure when other aspects of his character were forgotten, General Sir John Maxwell was lying tucked up in bed in an English nursing home and bemoaning his luck.

An intensely active man in his late fifties—impetuous and impatient—Maxwell was undergoing what he called an overhaul with the minimum of resignation. After eight months' experience of the workings of political intrigue as related to some pretty nasty in-fighting at the War Office—an experience so wildly frustrating that it had caused him to stomp angrily home from Egypt to pour out his woes to Kitchener in person —this present inactivity, caused by suspicions of a stone in the kidney, seemed to be the last straw.

Even when, a few days later, he was passed fit, Maxwell's thoughts continued to be gloomy.

"I am idle," he wrote to a friend, "and I fear am likely to be. The political people have got their knife into me."

Though the friend concerned—oddly, perhaps, a Salvation Army Commissioner—tried to argue him into a quieter frame of mind, Maxwell undoubtedly had cause for his complaint. He was a Kitchener man, and one of the very few to have had the "ear" of that remote and complex character. He was also very much the fighting general; the man who had managed to halt the Turks in what had appeared to be their irresistible drive towards the Delta. But with characteristic forthrightness he had clashed with the powers-that-be during the Dardanelles campaign; and caused offence in the Horse Guards by his comments when Sir Archibald Murray, the C.I.G.S. was sent to the Middle East in a position which, he felt, wastefully duplicated—and rivalled—his own.

Of Maxwell as a small boy, one of his Scottish uncles had written, "Fighting, to which he is addicted, gives his temper such a fierceness and impressiveness that he flies out on every occasion."

The description seemed pretty fair to apply to Maxwell the man.

"The way I have been treated!" he exploded, over Murray's appointment.

In vain did Kitchener try and persuade him to see reason. "You will find Murray an extremely nice officer to work with," he wrote with an unwonted note of pleading, "and I feel sure that no one can pull together the troops leaving Gallipoli as well as he can."

Maxwell refused to be so easily placated.

Also in vain was the political sop proffered. Titular "promotion" did not interest this dogged nonconformist. "My position becomes not only impossible but ridiculous," he complained to London.

"An impossible situation" had been created for him in Egypt, he explained to his friend the Commissioner, "and I could not with due regard to the public welfare continue to be an expense to the country there."

Maxwell left the Nile, where he had soldiered so long and devotedly—where the first shots he had fired in anger had been during the attempt to relieve Gordon at Khartoum—amid the cheers and tears of thousands of fellahin and the publicly expressed regret of "all that was the better element in the country's ruling class." This regret was reciprocated. The future "butcher" was in love with the land where he had held almost kingly sway; and his respect for its people—and his effort to serve them—appears to have been as genuine as it was unusual.

For a man who had exercised the power—in fact, if not in name—of viceroy, and had arbitrated in affairs that affected the destinies of the Islamic world, it was a bitter blow to be offered, back in an England that appeared to have forgotten his achievements, nothing more than the expectation of the command of an army corps. But Maxwell's professional grievances—at the administration and the War Office for the way in which he felt his career had been so arbitrarily curtailed—were not solely responsible for his current gloom.

This ruddy-faced, rather choleric man—in appearance so much the traditional brasshat as almost to be a caricature—was at heart a great family man, and devoted to his wife. Now she was ill, and about to face a serious operation.

In years to come, the General's biographer was to describe the former Miss Louise Bonynge as "the daughter of a worthy, wealthy and worldly-wise Irish gentleman, who after a long residence in America had become domiciled in England." By all who knew this talented woman, her conquest was agreed to be the happiest thing that had ever happened to Maxwell. And that plain-speaking soldier would have been the first to agree.

Throughout his career, Louise had been his confidante. She had shared his enthusiasm and sympathised with his reverses. She had felt as keenly about Egypt as he did, or at least she had never shown that she did not. Their daughter was given the classical Egyptian name of Philae.

Maxwell was well aware of his good fortune. Tough soldier —a professional—though he was, there was a certain streak of loneliness in the man, and sentiment too. However hard the campaigning, however bitter the political intriguing—such as the nice operation of influencing the departure of the Khedive "without fuss"—he never failed to keep Louise fully posted. Even the most mundane minutiae of his day-to-day business was recorded for her interest and support. Nor did he, in his fifties, fail to fret and fidget about how she was faring at home. There were occasions, said his friends, when "Conky"—a nickname bestowed upon him because of his rather generous nose—behaved as naively as a love-sick subaltern. But now this wife who meant so much to him was sick. And about to face a serious operation.

It was late on Wednesday when Maxwell was informed of his new command. He sailed for Ireland on Thursday night. In the meanwhile, characteristically he had "mugged up" every piece of information he could lay his hands on. Equally true to form, he had contrived to have sent to him—priority and in cypher—the latest news about Louise.

*　　*　　*

After the alarms of Wednesday, Thursday's dawn found the city almost unnaturally still. Among the garrisons of the distilleries, hitherto but lightly engaged, and divorced from news of the harsh realities that were changing the face of the rebellion in every sector but their own, this fact created yet another of the many misunderstandings to which they had been susceptible from the start.

Echoing the victorious mood of the headquarters staff on Monday, they concluded with splendid optimism that the foe had had enough: the lull must be the prelude to his seeking a settlement. In this belief they gaily made arrangements for a "victory dance", to be held the following Saturday. Among the Post Office commanders, however, there were few such pleasant illusions. The enemy, it was plain, was massing his forces for a fresh offensive: and this might be decisive—the blow at the heart.

With this in mind the indomitable Connolly decided to send detachments to secure houses in Mary Street to the rear of the G.P.O. and providing a link with Daly's men in the Four Courts. He had no sooner made this decision than the silence was sharply broken.

The shell came from an eighteen-pounder gun, dug into Westmoreland Road, the southern approach to the O'Connell Bridge. The men who fired it were parked between the Bank of Ireland and Trinity College, and found difficulty in "laying-on" to the Post Office itself because of the slight curve westwards taken by O'Connell Street, across the water, and the slight projection into the street of the Metropole, in the block to the immediate south of the rebel H.Q. and separated from it by Lower Abbey Street. It was on to this latter thoroughfare that they threw a ranging shot. Seldom can one shell have had more destructive results.

There was nothing that—for the first few minutes—marked the hit as anything special. Just a geyser of grey dust followed by billowing smoke and a slim finger of flame. Both to the gunners—and to Connolly—it was more or less a wasted effort: damaging a single building and creating yet another small fire: one small fire among many. But within a short space the flames had spread, and had caught great rolls of newsprint, stored for The Irish Times. It was the start of a chain reaction that was to wreck the city centre.

The Freeman's Journal, the Evening Telegraph, a printing works, the Coliseum Theatre—all these were to fall victim to the blaze before the day was out. It was to spread from Hopkin's Corner to the offices of the Tramway Company, in Cathedral Street, and then, reaching backward, envelop all the houses between Eden Quay and Lower Abbey Street. The Hibernian Academy, the H.Q. of The Irish Cyclist, Mooney's pub, the Dublin Bread Company—no respecter of the character or type of property it encountered, it was to run in tributaries of molten red, enveloping abandoned barricades, which it used to leap streets and alleys, destroying all that stood in its way: a no-man's land of fire through which neither side could venture. And yet, at its birth, no one could even guess at the horror that it would bring. Instead, the sound of the shell that was to sire this devouring monster was noted only because of the calm that preceded it; and the way in which it heralded a resumption of the British attack.

*   *   *

Just after noon a new sound echoed through O'Connell Street, a sound distinctive from the harsh cacophony of the rifles and machine-guns and the screaming wail of shells from the guns across the river . . . a sound similar to thunder but seemingly coming from beneath the ground . . . houses swayed and trembled, then steadied again.

A rebel engineer came into the road centre and regardless of bullets, cursed fluently and long. The Nelson Pillar was still intact. Trust them to do a solid job of building, a century ago. Morosely he wondered whether to try again: but other commitments now weighed heavily on the technical wing at headquarters. Again, the possibility of the Pillar serving as a point of aim for British warships seemed to have become more remote than it was thought to be before. Why should the enemy bother to bring in the Navy, when he now could bombard as much as he liked from the shore? All the same, the Pillar's resistance irked him. The Admiral looked . . . well so bloody *superior!*

At the foot of the street, the O'Connell Monument was similarly defiant of current malice and twentieth century weapons of war. It had become—so it was felt—the special target of the machine-gun nests now installed in Trinity yet, remarkably, suffered little real damage. The worst wound sustained by the Emancipator was a bullet hole in the ear: just as well, it was said, or the noise would have made him turn in his grave. Among the masses little love was lost for the "Sinn Feiners" who had brought such trouble upon the city.

The previous night an Irish Resident Magistrate—Lynch-Robinson—had completed, revolver in pocket, an adventurous journey from Donegal to see how his wife was faring, on holiday with her parents in the suburb of Foxrock. To get there, he had by-passed the rebels in the city by proceeding through Leixlip, and making his way through the Dublin mountains. "When I got on to the high ground looking down on the city it was perfectly plain that there were the devil's own delights going on there," he later recorded in his memoirs. "Fires were burning all over the place, some gunboat or other was lobbing shells into Liberty Hall . . . and one could hear the rattle of small arms and see occasional shell-bursts in the centre of the city. Along the roads there were people who had come to watch who all displayed strong feelings about the Sinn Feiners. They're as bad as the Germans, so they are . . . destroying the people . . . murdering everyone."

The Irish Catholic was already preparing for its attack on Pearse—"a crazy and insolent schoolmaster". The insurgents it was to describe as "an extraordinary combination of rogues

131

and fools." Stronger words were employed by the people from the tenements, pelting prisoner Volunteers with rotten fruit and chunks of brick. Yet, here and there were signs of a change of heart.

Ernie O'Malley, son of loyalist parents and, until the rising, itching to join his brother at the Front, recalls the visit of a family friend, a Dublin Fusilier. "He drank his large glass of whiskey and was eagerly listened to. He was an authority. His officers had told him, 'Every man you see in green uniform, regard him as a German soldier, as an invader, and shoot him down.' We examine all suspects," he said, "and a bruise on anyone's shoulder means that he has been using a long barrelled Mauser. I'd like to stack them up against a wall instead of making them prisoners." The soldier, says O'Malley "was hailed by many who were anxious to shake hands as he walked away . . ."

What the Fusilier did not know, however, was that young Ernie—who originally had pondered about joining the defenders of Trinity and fighting the rebels—had himself been using a Mauser only the night before. Not a single-shot "Howth" model at that, but the latest magazine type.

The story of the transformation of O'Malley from the role of young student to future chief of staff of the I.R.A. in the battles that followed the rising and its suppression, had begun when he had walked up and down the back garden of his home and found that the distant sounds of firing "aroused strange echoes" in his head. "They meant something personal, they made me angry. The men down there were right, that I felt sure of. They had a purpose which I did not share. But no one had the right to Ireland except the Irish. In the city, Irishmen were fighting British troops against long odds. I was going to help them in some way."

That same evening O'Malley met a former classmate, an ardent member of the Gaelic League. "I know where there's a rifle," said the boy. "My father was given it, as a present from a soldier who had brought it back from the front."

A few hours later the pair were sniping at British pockets on the canal bridge . . .

O'Malley was one of the first of many who were to find in the rebels' defiance a stirring of the spirit that they might otherwise never have known, and the reversal of loyalties that, hitherto, they had taken for granted. It was a process that, of course, was to split families down the middle.

In between fighting the Kaiser's High Seas Fleet, an uncle of the author wrote angrily home: "I am ashamed that such

132

people (the rebels) should dare to call themselves Irish. Had I my way we would have made short work of them. Our 6-inch guns would have set the whole pack running!" Two months later he was killed in action. Two years later his younger brother was "on the run"—as a diehard republican!

On Thursday, had the rebel leaders but known it, their mystique of what Connolly called "redemption through blood" was already beginning to achieve results—had they but known it. At the time, however, Thursday did not seem to be their lucky day.

* * *

In the South Dublin Union the 2/8th Sherwood Foresters were again in action, and Captain Oates—the Colonel's son —was distinguishing himself in close hand-to-hand fighting with Kent's men, now driven back from all their outposts bar one and confined to one block of the Nurses's Home.

To the east, the neck of the bag had been drawn tight around de Valera's contingent, isolating them in their positions around Boland's Mill and the railway line.

In the centre, Jacobs' had been cut off by the establishment of the cordon from Kingsbridge to the Castle and the ring that now contracted around St Stephen's Green, where Mallin's men fought on among the grisly exhibits of the College of Surgeons, and the Countess was lamenting the lack of stabbing instruments, to be used in in-fighting when ammunition ran out.

North of the Liffey, a tenuous line of communications still extended westwards to Daly's battalion, holding the Four Courts and the maze of working-class streets to the north west: but pressure was building up and concerted attack seemed imminent. Eastwards the British had reached a point only 200 yards from the doorstep of rebel H.Q.

Of provincial reactions the only positive news came from Enniscorthy, and this was not of a nature to give the leadership much encouragement. The R.I.C. and local residents still held out in the police barracks and others keypoints, despite the fact that, at the start of the rising, the R.I.C. men had only thirty rounds apiece. The clue to their prolonged defiance lay in the fact that a recent arms raid had yielded them over a thousand rounds of ammunition, originally destined for the Volunteers. "It came in handy," the local Inspector was later smugly to record. "It happened to be of a type that fitted our own rifles."

Luck—in addition to material and numbers—was on the

side of the British that Thurdsay. It was the day their bullets
at last tracked-down James Connolly.

*   *   *

Never leaving others to do what he wouldn't do himself,
Connolly went in person with the detachment he had ordered
into the Mary Street area. No sooner had the rebels left the
Post Office, than they came under heavy fire. They travelled
at the double, hugging walls and shattered shop fronts; and
the trip was completed without a single casualty. Not a single
casualty until, having seen his men duly "settled", Connolly
started his return journey. He felt a savage blow in the arm.
Hit!

It was typical of the man that his first thought at that
moment should be to hide his vulnerability from his followers
—it might make bad propaganda.

With deliberate nonchalance he slowed his pace, and almost
sauntered into the Post Office. Then, very discreetly, he called
for Captain Mahoney, an Indian Army M.O. who had been
taken prisoner the preceding Tuesday. He had his wound
dressed behind a screen, and swore the Captain to secrecy.
No one must know that James Connolly could be open as the
next man to the accidents of war!

It was in keeping with this spirit of deception that the
Labour leader only minutes later embarked on yet another
of his cheer-raising inspections of the defence posts. He was
as exuberant as ever . . . talking victory as ever . . . and was,
to the Volunteers, as fit as ever. Then, typically, he pressed
his luck too far.

In the afternoon, in an attempt to provide an additional
cover against British infiltration Connolly ordered a group of
Volunteers to occupy the offices of the Sunday Independent.
Again he insisted on making the trip himself; and again there
were no casualties until the time he started back. This time
he was hit in the leg.

Connolly, dazed, found he had flopped into the gutter of
Middle Abbey Street. He tried to get to his feet, but the pain
was frightful. He started to shout, but his voice was not heard
above the chatter of the machine-guns. He was on his own.
It seemed to take him an age to crawl on all fours to Prince's
Street, a short turning next to the Post Office. There, lookouts
spotted him, and brought him in.

There was no longer any chance of hiding the fact that the
virile Connolly was wounded. The news created among the
staff an atmosphere of mourning. He was in desperate pain,

134

and must rest—or be sent to hospital. Mahoney and his republican colleagues, in professional alliance when it came to the task of saving lives, agreed most emphatically on this: but the patient would not hear of it.

Emerging from the anaesthetic, Connolly made two notable remarks. To Kathleen Carney, his devoted secretary, he said: "The fellow who fired that shot did the best day's work yet for England . . ." To Captain Mahoney he wisecracked: "You're the best capture we've yet had."

It wasn't long before he was again on a tour of inspection —but this time he was wheeled through the building in his bed.

* * *

By nightfall the garrisons of the Post Office, the Metropole to its south, and the isolated posts that represented all that was left of the rebel line in O'Connell Street looked out upon an awesome spectacle of demoniac destruction. The blaze was devouring the entire east side of the street, and raging on, completely unchecked. The British guns had ceased firing, but the night was noise-filled with the thunder of tumbling roofs and walls. To the sick Plunkett, who had dragged himself to the roof to watch the scene, it inspired classical comparisons. Rome burning? Or Moscow? Which was the most apt?

* * *

For Arthur Griffith, the distant sight of the inferno was too much . . . too much to stand and look at without *doing*.

He mounted his bicycle, and pedalled over to Rathfarnham. There he saw the "deposed" leader, MacNeill. Sinking all their differences, and grievances, the two men then reached agreement.

Regardless of the consequences, they would call for a general rising. They were, however, too late.

CHAPTER THIRTEEN

"From the sea it looked as if the entire city of Dublin was in flames," wrote Maxwell to his wife, "but when we got to the North Wall it was not quite as bad as that, yet a great part of the Liffey was burning. Bullets were flying about, the crackling of musketry and machine-gun fire ringing out every other minute."

The rebels he described as being "in a ring fence" and he prophesied that, by the next day, the position would be "much clearer." Forebodingly, though he added "a lot of men will be knocked over."

The new C-in-C. had made the trip to Ireland by night. He had travelled to what was traditionally the residence of the Commanding Officer in Ireland—the Royal Hospital at Kilmainham—in the centre of a three-car convoy, moving slowly without lights through streets strewn with debris. "Those infernal rebels," he discovered, had got "a lot of rifles and apparently a fair amount of ammunition too." Sniping never stopped. Despite such preoccupations, however, he still found time to fidget about Louise's health. "I am glad you are doing all right," he wrote, "but mind, no setbacks. And *do* try to do what the doctor orders!"

*   *   *

His domestic epistle completed, Maxwell put it aside, for inclusion in the bag that would carry his official despatches, and turned once more to the practical business of implementing the mandate that had torn him from Louise, and brought him to restore law and order—as he saw it—to this flame-lit and shell-torn city.

There was nothing in the phrasing of the terms of reference that accompanied his appointment to cause him, at this moment, any particular misgivings. There was to be no damn political interference—*that* seemed plain!—in the way he conducted things for the good of unhappy Ireland. He had in fact a free hand. H.M. Government "desired" that, as G.O.C., General Maxwell "use all such measures as may in his opinion be necessary for the suppression of insurrection." There were none of the restrictive ifs and buts that one usually expected to find inserted by the "frocks." On a gesture unprecedented perhaps since the days of Cromwell, he had been given "full plenary powers." Practically the powers of military dictatorship. In a double somersault born of panic, the Government of Ireland, so it seemed, had not only reversed its previous policy of laissez-faire—or "shilly-shallying" as Macready had called it—it had also, in the process, contrived to dispose of itself.

"All such measures as may in his opinion be necessary . . ."

A more subtle, or less honest, man than Maxwell might have seen in the very looseness of the phrase not only the panic of authority in urgent need of quick rescue from the mess it had got itself into, but also a method of shelving responsibility for any future embarrassments—embarrassments arising from the way in which that rescue might be conducted.

* * *

"Father was faced with a formidable problem," Philae has since recalled, "in which he had to appear as a cold-hearted tyrant whereas he was in reality one of the kindest and most tender-hearted of men . . ."

This filial view of the G.O.C.'s disposition and character is one that the Irish "malcontents" would have found very difficult to credit.

Within an hour of his arrival at Kilmainham—where he found that "neither the Lord Lieutenant nor the Chief Secretary particularly appreciate being under my orders"— the new leader started off on the task of making it quite clear to everyone just where he stood: and where *they* stood as well.

With maddening tact he informed Lord Wimborne and Mr Birrell, "that I did not mean to interfere *unless it was necessary*, and I hoped they *would do all that I asked them to*." Next, having examined Lowe's military dispositions—of his conversation with the unlucky General Friend he preserves a perhaps chivalrous silence—he drew up, in the best siege-style, a formal Proclamation.

"The most vigorous measures will be taken by me to stop the loss of life and damage to property which certain mis-guided persons are causing by armed resistance to the law," Maxwell promised his new charges, the citizens of Dublin. And then, in the very next sentence, he added firmly, "If necessary I shall not hesitate to destroy all buildings within any area occupied by the rebels . . ."

The insurgents were to make gleeful use of the "Irishness" of the G.O.C.'s style of delivery—and yet his two promises, though in a juxtaposition that could rightly be described as unfortunate, were not as incompatible as they sounded. Like every other military officer in the city, Maxwell was preoccupied with fears of German intervention. He was genuinely appalled by the way in which the rebellion had been allowed to drag on. As a soldier he could see small profit in his engaging in a form of battle where the pattern of tactics employed was dictated by the tactics used by the rebels themselves. He wanted a quick decision, by employing maximum force: including artillery. Dublin was the nerve centre of revolt. The "limbs" of revolt in the provinces would be incapable of menacing movement once their directing-source was no more. They would wither and die.

The one weakness in Maxwell's line of reasoning was that —to quote a rather different metaphor—he was in danger of throwing the baby out with the bath-water.

* * *

It was on Daly's front that Friday's hammer-blows flew heaviest. The streets around the Four Courts trembled to the blast of the shells. Shrapnel crackled overhead, raining steel across the housetops. Doggedly, the rebels braced themselves to face the assault.

Outside Riley's Fort near Upper King Street the captured lance still streamed the tricolour defiantly before the eyes of the British. Twice it was blown down by blast: and twice put up again. Inside the main court of justice, they had blocked the windows with the loot of the library. Hundreds of hefty legal tomes, latched together with wire and string. These proved to be "most satisfactory"—recalls a Volunteer officer—in keeping out the salvoes of machine-gun bullets that were now being pumped into the building from positions across the river and in a nearby graveyard. But when the eighteen-pounders of the Royal Artillery began to score "even the dome appeared to shake." Fresh fires now blossomed amid the cinders left by the old. They grew and prospered. The Fire Brigade, which until then had functioned with glorious impartiality in both Crown and rebel zones of influence, could no longer operate. Its hoses were so many colanders. Its engines riddled by bullets. Desperately the Dublin Fire Chief now pleaded with the British for permission to take even these shattered vehicles to the scene of the threatened holocaust. "Too dangerous" came the reply.

An historian of the South Staffs has described the King Street area as occupied by "innumerable houses of the smaller

138

kind, and shops of the cheaper sort. If it was not actually a slum it may certainly be described as a congested area, penetrated by an infinite number of passages and alleys and more nearly resembling a rabbit-warren than a battlefield."

Daly's defensive system was clever in the extreme. "The street", recalls another member of the South Staffs, "was defended by a series of barricades, crude affairs composed largely of household furniture. But the strength of them consisted in the fact that they reinforced, or were reinforced by, the sniping posts in the houses of the street. The barricades delayed the troops, and made them a steady target; the sniping posts being manned for the most part by isolated riflemen, shooting from second floor windows. The rebels had so situated themselves as to be able to inflict maximum casualties on the British troops with minimum loss to themselves."

It was into this area—the hard-core of the north western defences—that the military, in haste for a decision, now chose to launch their greatest attack.

Whole barricades were blasted away by shells. The streets shook to explosions, and the tread of armoured lorries, packed with infantry, used in an attempt to bypass the rebel snipers dominating the crossroads. The fires spread. Yet it was not on the men and boys of Daly's "Fighting First", nor on the dour soldiers from the English Midland cities, crouching and zig-zagging their way through the bullet-swept battle zone that the worst tortures of the day were now inflicted. *Those* were reserved for the hapless and hopeless non-combatants. The thousands and tens of thousands of folk who crowded the filthy cellars of the tenements around which the tide of conflict surged, receded and came on again.

It was Wimborne who, as Viceroy, had first declared Martial Law. It was Maxwell who was to drive home what it meant. He ordered his troops to fight their way through the outposts; so as to throw two cordons around the main centres of rebel resistance, the G.P.O. and the Four Courts area. These would then be isolated, and bombarded into submission.

The general did not seem unduly concerned about the fate of the residents of the "war-zone" districts. He had already warned them to flee from the wrath to come. In his Proclamation, he had stressed there would be safe-conduct for the uncommitted, and, conscientiously had gone into details. Women and children should report at the nearest checkpoint, where they would then be escorted to a safe area. Males would be screened, but, if found to be free of association with the rebels, would promptly be turned loose to join their families.

Unfortunately, however, Maxwell had overlooked one small detail when preparing his characteristically thorough manifesto. The near impossibility of his instructions getting through to the people to whom they were addressed.

Officers with megaphones were sent to certain of the checkpoints—to summon the rebels to unconditional surrender, and the law-abiding to safety. The Government printing-press turned out copies of the proclamation by the thousand, for distribution throughout the city. But megaphones could not be heard in the cellars—not by ears blocked to the thunder of the guns. And the "postal service" extended for only so far as a soldier could live.

The people were in a wretched condition by now. They had been without food since Monday. They had been without light since early Tuesday morning. And, for the past forty-eight hours, hundreds of them had been deprived of water. There were fears of gas-leaks. Fears of fire. Rats roamed up from the part-blocked sewers. In such circumstances the brisk and soldier-like prose of Maxwell, prepared in the elegant setting of Kilmainham, went unheard.

*　　*　　*

"While fighting continued under conditions so confused and so trying it is possible that some innocent citizens were shot," the G.O.C. was later to admit. "It was impossible to distinguish between those who were, or had been, firing upon the troops and those who, for various causes, *chose* to remain on the scene of the fighting . . . instead of leaving their houses and passing through the cordon."

"Chose"? For most of the denizens of the working class districts of Dublin there was very little "choice" that Friday morning. They "stayed put" through ignorance. Also they "stayed put" through fear. They didn't know where to report. They didn't know what a cordon meant, let alone where the cordons were. On the maps of the military such dividing lines were drawn in thick red lines. In the minds of the people, the division between occupation zones was marked only by movement—the movement of armed men, storming into their hiding places—and moments of hope, or fear, or downright terror.

An officer of the 2/6th Sherwood Foresters has since described the reactions of his battalion to the new search routine in what he calls the "rabbit warren of alleys" in East Side.

"The women," he writes, "were incoherent with fear, and what with these hysterical women, screeching children and the unpleasant task of searching the filthiest homes we had ever seen, the task was anything but pleasant. No arms were found, and few men."

In the King Street area, this sort of search—conducted within minutes of savage in-fighting—imposed on the South Staffs a strain that was to prove unbearable.

*　　*　　*

The 2/6th South Staffordshire Regiment had been sent to relieve the Sherwoods after the battle of Mount Street Bridge, and had then been engaged by de Valera's outposts, near Boland's Mills. It had been a matter of sniping rather than close combat, and though casualties had been incurred they were relatively light. Lowe, seeking to implement Maxwell's directive and draw a cordon around the stubbornly defended Four Courts area, had therefore chosen to bring forward this relatively fresh unit rather than expose to further loss the pathetically weakened Sherwood Foresters. The initial objective would be for the 2/6th to link hands with the 2/5th, already working their way around the northern flank of Daly's force.

From the Brigadier's simple decision was to stem one of the ugliest incidents in the history of the Rising.

From the moment of their arrival, the South Staffs were under concentrated fire. It was directed at them from the roofs of Upper King Street, the corners of the road junctions, the alleys that led to the Four Courts and the Quays. Progress was slow, and tempers razor-thin.

Daly had thrown up a barricade between Linenhall Street and Coleraine Street, opposite Riley's Fort.

In the first assault Lieutenant J. Sheppard was seriously wounded, and a civilian medical officer killed. Casualties among the men were "heavy"; but the Staffordshires continued to attack. Two platoons of "C" company were sent forward. Then they were reinforced by two more. The barricade remained unbroken.

Right through the hot afternoon, in the reek of the buildings that burned in Linenhall Street, the battalion continued its frustrated attempts to move forward. High morale gave place to sullen rage. The men's scant training had been for trench warfare. They had never bargained on

141

this deadly inch-by-inch series of starts and stops, or battle fought in an area so lacking in elbow-room that one determined man could hold up a platoon.

There was a change of tactics. "A" company was brought forward in armoured lorries, and seized houses at the junction of North King Street and Church Street. From this point they started to burrow forward through walls of adjoining houses. But progress was slow, and stopped short by rebel fire in the very last lap of all, a few yards of cleared ground just short of the barricade.

By nightfall, the South Staffs felt that they had had enough of it. They were frustrated, angry, and some of them—as it proved—were ready for murder. Rumours of treachery spread through the ranks. Imaginations ran riot. It was even said that priests who had visited the area had done so as Sinn Fein spies, carrying pistols beneath their cassocks. When houses blazed through the dark, it was said that the rebels had deliberately set them alight: to silhouette the soldiers against the glare.

Time and time again the tired men had vainly attempted to clear Shouldice's garrison out of Riley's. Time and time again they had been repulsed. And now came a report of snipers being concealed in nearby houses.

Led by a Sergeant—"He ran amok," Maxwell later confided to Kitchener——a group of soldiers smashed their way into the small houses of Upper King Street. They tore husbands from the wives, fathers from their daughters, and sons from their mothers. They dragged them away into the cellars and the side streets.

It was a month before their bodies were recovered. There were twenty-two of them.

*   *   *

"The smoke of many buildings on fire darkens the glorious sunshine as one looks towards the heart of the city. And all this at high noon, in the capital of Ireland!" So mourned an Irish newspaper reporter, witnessing the city burn from the hills, nine miles away.

Closeup, the picture was even more tragic.

Down in O'Connell Street, the men in headquarters looked out on a scene of appalling devastation. A scene set in a man-made twilight: the smoke that rose from the burning.

The overhead wires of the tramway, severed by shell and bullet, draped a crazy lacework over the bare ribs of Clery's and appeared to lock with the barbed wire apron, now in several parts smashed down, that stretched from the front of the Post Office.

Kelly's, on the corner of the bridge, jettisoned a great gout of vivid flame that spread and contracted in spasms as it was caught by the blast of the shells. Down the entire length and breadth of the street that, a few days before, had been one of the most elegant in Europe, bullets sparked angrily on pavements, walls and kerbs.

The air was windless, yet the roar of the blaze, and the strength of the draught that the blaze itself had created, gave to those few who ventured out of headquarters—to scurry with despatches to the Metropole—the impression of being caught in a stupendous gale.

Unburied, the dead horses marking the fate of the Lancers' charge stank to high heaven: each of them a bloated dunghill, swarming with flies.

To at least one observer, the melancholy vista of O'Connell Street was symbolic of the fate of all the high hopes of Monday: symbolic also of the future of the Cause on which those hopes had been pinned. It took Padraic Pearse to see beyond the immediate ruin, and glimpse, in present defeat, the seed of victory.

The proclamation he had penned a few hours earlier, was significant of this . . . and expressive of the far horizons to which his eyes were turned.

The employment of propaganda to stiffen current resistance —flagging in face of the disheartening facts—took second place now to the message to posterity.

After an account of the military situation that was candid, down to earth, and fulfilled the crying need for information, the Commanding General of the Irish Republican Army, and President of the Irish Provisional Government, used words that would spur those who read them in the future.

"I desire now, lest I may not have an opportunity later, to pay homage to the gallantry of the soldiers of Irish Freedom who have during the past four days been writing with fire and steel the most glorious chapter in the later history of Ireland. Justice can never be done to their heroism, to their discipline, to their great and unconquerable spirit in the midst of peril and death. Let me, who have led them into

143

this, speak, in my own and in my fellow commanders' names, and in the name of Ireland present and to come, their praise, and ask them who come after them to remember them. . . ."

The virtues of the men who had followed Pearse into battle were to be immortalised, to inspire successors.

"No man has complained, no man has asked 'Why?' Each . . . has spent himself, happy to pour out his strength for Ireland and for freedom. If they do not win this fight, they will at least have deserved to win it. But win it they will, *although they may win it in death . . .*"

There was more in similar vein.

The Volunteers had made Dublin's name "Splendid among the names of cities" . . . which, though perhaps hard for suffering Dubliners to appreciate at the moment, was great stuff for the future.

James Connolly "lies wounded, but is still the guiding brain of our resistance."

Pearse was generous even as regards the "fatal countermanding order", which, as he explained, had prevented a simultaneous rising throughout the country. "Both Eoin MacNeill and we have acted in the best interests of Ireland."

In conclusion, he said: "For my part, as to anything I have done in this, I am not afraid to face either the judgment of God, or the judgment of posterity."

Later, it was the wounded Connolly's turn to address the little garrison. He made a tour of inspection—he was wheeled around the Post Office in his bed—and then decided that he, too, should issue a written exhortation.

Unlike Pearse, the Labour leader was more occupied with the need to keep the current fight going than the prospect of preparing the way for a bigger fight in the future. Outrageously, unrepentingly, and while in great personal pain, he boasted of victory—all along the line.

"Not a day passes without seeing fresh postings of Irish soldiers eager to do battle for the old cause," he wrote. "The British army . . . are afraid to advance to the attack or storm any positions held by our forces. The slaughter they have suffered in the last few days has totally unnerved them, and they dare not attempt again an infantry attack on our positions."

Good rousing stuff, this. But there was even better to follow. News of successes in the provinces . . . reassurance that "our allies in Germany and kinsmen in America are straining every nerve to hasten matters" . . . and, finally: "Courage, boys, we are winning, and in the hour of victory let us not forget the splendid women who have everywhere stood by us and cheered us on. Never had man or woman a grander cause, never was a cause more grandly served."

The last sentence was probably the only one that James Connolly believed to be true.

It was 4.30 when the first shell hit the Post Office.

CHAPTER FOURTEEN

That first shell caught the roof alight. Other shells fanned the flames. Soon the whole cupola was incandescent red, with giant tongues of fire darting out from its shattered sides.

Heroically, a party of Volunteers crawled spider-like across the steel girders that had held the now molten glass, unwinding a web of hoses behind them, over the skeleton of the dome. It was terrifying work, this dizzy progress over the inferno below, and made even more so by the persistent British machine-gunners.

The O'Rahilly, loyal to MacNeill, had rushed the Countermanding Order to the provinces that had struck the first, but decisive blow, against hopes of rebel success. But his dislike of a rising had not prevented this chivalrous and lionhearted man from himself taking up arms when he knew it could not be stopped. Now—not for the first time—he showed his superb mettle.

The blaze had done something to Pearse that nothing had ever done before—it had shaken his composure and caused him temporarily to lose his head. With little or no sleep behind him for the past four days, he rounded on Plunkett, who promptly answered back. It took the O'Rahilly to stop the shouting-match, and muster their shocked followers into disciplined action. Time after time again—conspicuous by reason of his giant build and his heat-scorched tyrolean hat, which no regulation would force him to abandon—this fearless fellow led bucket chains forward to the fringes of the fire. But though they managed to slow the blaze, he and his men were quite unable to stop it.

At last the battle in the dome had to be brought to a close —with huge portions of the walls breaking and falling into the street below. But the O'Rahilly then attacked from another front. As the fire spread into the top storey he had ladders lashed to the walls. Men climbed them to the ceiling in which they punctured holes for the hoses. Repeatedly he led them to fresh exertions: "When we looked at him," a Volunteer recalls, "we saw all that was best in what we were fighting for."

Pearse, tranquil again, now issued his orders for the day.

All units in O'Connell Street were to muster at the G.P.O. for an attempt to break through the British lines after dark towards the north-west *and "join forces with our comrades in the provinces."*

It was to be his last order but one.

* * *

In the Metropole, its walls torn by shell-fire some two score weary men greeted Pearse's command with unrestrained enthusiasm. First lap of the escape, they were told, must be made across Prince's Street, which divided the hotel from the G.P.O. There they would muster with the main body of their comrades and move from the side door of the Post Office out into Henry Street.

"No longer," a Volunteer shouted, "will we wait here like rats in a trap!"

They were singing as they waited for the word to go.

Their entry into the smoke-filled street, however, provided them with a grim foretaste of the perils that lay ahead. Pearse had ordered the remaining women of the garrison to leave and, under flag of truce, surrender to the British. With them they were to take the majority of the wounded. But the emergence of a group of these unhappy people coincided with that of the departure of the men from the Metropole and there followed a brief period of complete confusion and fear.

The barricade at the end of the street had been set alight by the shells, and the women panicked. Several minutes passed before they could be persuaded to move on, and space be made for the Metropole men to dash across the street into the blazing headquarters. When they arrived there, their spirits were at near bottom.

Night seemed to be long in coming. And even when it did, the word to move had still to be awaited. In the meanwhile, except for the fire-fighters there was little to do but stand by, and look around one. The spectacle did not inspire.

The headquarters of the high hopes of Easter Monday was now in terrible shape. In the main assembly area the only light came from the flames, roaring in the upper storeys and casting their radiance through a shell hole in the ceiling. Smoke eddied across the slumped and dejected lines of the rebel survivors, as though the place was filled with a particularly obnoxious fog. Everyone hacked and coughed. Depression and defeat were etched on blackened faces as deeply as the lines of their tiredness and stress.

147

In one corner, a group of men were kneeling and saying the rosary. In another, a quarrel broke out.

"We're betrayed!" yelled a member of the Citizen Army. "Pearse's lot have allowed us to be trapped!"

Grabbing his rifle, he started for the door. "Who'll come with me, and so some bloody *fighting?*"

A vivid flash lit the room. It was followed by a crackling hail of shrapnel, falling through the hole in the ceiling. Somewhere a man screamed, and there was a cry for stretcher-bearers. The Citizen Army man sheepishly pushed his way back into the crowd.

"Sorry," he said to some angry Volunteers. "We're all in this mess together."

From outside came a rumbling noise that was different to the sharp crumpph of the shells. A landslide of falling masonry, from a collapsing wall. And then, in the stunned hush that followed it, a rich tenor voice began to sing.

"Soldiers are we,
Whose lives are pledged to Ireland
Sworn to be free,
Of the despote or the slave . . ."

Other voices joined in—it would have done Kearney good to have heard them and in a moment the garrison had recovered its fighting spirit.

* * *

"Silence all round save for the distant crackle of the flames," wrote a reporter, from a vantage point four miles away. "It was as though a bar had been laid down between Dublin and all humanity till the account of the rebels is paid. Minute by minute and hour by hour we watched the city burning . . ."

Maxwell, who had moved from the Royal Hospital to take a closer look at things from Dublin Castle, would have given much to penetrate just what was hapening behind that wall of fire. He had reinforced the cordons to the northwest and now planned to inject fresh man-power into the South Staffs, whose slow progress in the Four Courts area was causing some concern. Would the rebels surrender? Or would they try and run?

It was not only in the area held by the rebels, every minute contracting still further to the pressures of fire and bullet, that there was confusion and taut nerves. Already staff officers were worrying about a rumour that had reached them of the murder by an English officer of a prominent pacifist, and four innocent civilians, two of them out-and-out opponents to everything that the rebellion stood for. The man concerned had gone "mad", it was whispered privately— but there would be hell to pay, once the full story got out.

Steps to end the endemic of looting might also be criticised as "going a bit too far." In one area officers had ordered that looters be shot, and their bodies exposed as an "example."

But Maxwell was oblivious, as yet, to such symptoms of trigger-happiness. He was concentrating on the main objective, the destruction of the rebel command.

When night fell the British pickets in the cordons around the flaming centre of revolt stood-to. Machine-guns were trained on road intersections to the Post Office's rear. Search-lights were brought up to illuminate likely routes between the defenders of the Four Courts and the rebels who—*how* nobody knew!—still managed to stick it out in the flaming hell that the guns had made of their granite-walled H.Q.

* * *

Inside the Post Office, the rebels continued to sing. It was, says a survivor, "a quite incredible proceeding." Yet, at the time it seemed the thing to do. One virtue of using one's voice was that the sound combated the frightening noise of the flames.

Certainly it must have served as some sort of safety valve for the pent up fears of those few of the men who know what was happening beneath their feet.

Large quantities of gelignite, and the entire reserve of the garrison's home-made bombs had been deposited in the central basement of the Post Office. Now even this strongpoint was beginning to glow with heat. The explosives were being moved to a yard in the rear.

It was tricky work. With highly volatile material. And once again the O'Rahilly was the prime organiser of it all.

Sluicing away with a hose at the sparks that, tossed by the blast of shells and the draught of the flames up top, glowed like minute stars against the shaft to the basement, he seemed to his chain of chosen volunteers like some monstrous will-o'-the-wisp, in a hundred places at once. But even the O'Rahilly could not conquer by his energy the ill luck that dogged the Post Office on Friday. Only half of the store had been cleared when the water ceased to flow.

149

His face as black as a negro's he led his team to the surface. The time had come to get out.

* * *

To a little group of Headquarters officers Pearse was detailing his plan.

Once out in neighbouring Henry Street, the Volunteers would pass on their right the bottom of Moore Lane—screened by a barricade from the bullets of a British force installed in the northern end. Then they would advance up the next turning to their right—Moore Street—to their immediate objective, the premises of Williams and Woods. He had selected this place as a temporary H.Q. because it was one of the few tall buildings in the city centre to be untouched by the blaze. There the force would re-group, then resume its advance to the north.

It sounded quite feasible.

With typical impulsiveness, the chivalrous O'Rahilly chimed in. He would take thirty men and dash up Moore Street right away—to prevent the route being occupied by the enemy.

This was agreed.

"Either a glorious victory, or a glorious death boys," said the O'Rahilly to his men.

Pistol in hand, he led the way.

It was only a few minutes later that a young Volunteer, Willy MacLaughlin, came in to the Post Office to protest to Pearse: "Why strike for the north? Why not let's go westward along Henry Street and link up with the Four Courts?"

Pearse hesitated.

"The British," said MacLaughlin, "are in force in Great Britain Street. They have built a barricade, and can fire down Moore Street!"

Galvanised into action, Pearse yelled: "Recall the O'Rahilly!"

It was too late.

* * *

Before turning the corner into Moore Street the O'Rahilly gave a final briefing to his picked command. They would split into two groups. One would advance along the right hand pavement. He would lead on the left. Within seconds they had caught the full blast of the Sherwood Foresters, a platoon of whom had occupied the upper end of the street. The attack force scattered. The attack withered. The street was studded with dead and wounded. The O'Rahilly re-grouped his men in the slender shelter of a side turning. And then decided to attack again.

This time the little force got half way to the barricade. When they were forced by the Sherwoods' fire to halt, the O'Rahilly had been hit—and so had twenty-one of the thirty who had followed him. He crawled into a shop entrance and wrote a brief note to his wife: "I was hit leading a rush. I got more than one bullet I think." And then, with his face towards the barricade, he died . . .

* * *

Thwarted in his attempt to warn the Moore Street detachment, MacLaughlin found himself at the head of the main force, now on Pearse's orders, starting the planned "breakout." From the start, things went wrong. The Moore Lane barricade fulfilled its role in masking the rebel approach from the Crown Forces at its top, but British snipers raked them from the dome of the Rotunda, over in Parnell Square. Confusion set in. As MacLaughlin, followed by Collins, attempted to sprint across the bottom of Moore Street—to pursue his plan of a march to the Four Courts area—a group of Volunteers conforming to Pearse's original directive stormed up the street, and were chopped down by the British guns.

In a moment the scattered survivors had gone to earth, dazed and bewildered, in the small terrace houses to the left and right of the street. A new H.Q. was hurriedly set up in Cogan's, a grocer's shop on the corner.

Said someone despairingly: "My God, we're boxed in again!"

* * *

Connolly, on his stretcher had insisted on being one of the last men out, but now as the machine-guns in Great Britain Street (now re-named Parnell Street) carved a deep furrow down the length and breadth of the rebels' escape route, Pearse stood alone before the altar of the sacrifice.

Men saw him silhouetted against great globules of red and orange, expanding and contracting in spasms, depending on how the draught caught them. For several minutes he waited there—thinking *what* no one shall ever know—then joined by his brother Willie, and survivors of the team that had earlier escorted a group of women and wounded to hospital, he turned away.

A terrifying rumble came from inside the doomed Post

Office. Collapsing floors stuck upwards a myriad specks of fire. As Pearse hastened his pace a crackling flare shifted the shadows thrown by the buildings in Moore Lane with the remorseless totality of a sponge pressed over a slate. Momentarily, he tripped. And the cry went up "he's shot." Regaining his balance he came on.

Pearse had slipped at the spot where, a few minutes earlier a teenager had run beside Connolly's stretcher, to place himself between his chief and the British bullets. Exhaustedly, the Citizen Army man had raised his head, then said to Winifred Carney: "We can't fail now—such lads will never forget."

* * *

Pearse, reaching Cogan's, was about to give the command "fix bayonets" and lead a charge to clear the British barricade at the top of Moore Street, when second thoughts prevailed. Ahead of him lay the bodies of those who had followed the O'Rahilly's gallant example: an attack in the open street was doomed to fail. Instead, he decided that the column should advance through the terraced houses and tunnel their way through the dividing lines. Progress was painfully slow, and, all the time, he was worried about James Connolly.

Owing to the narrowness of the gaps that had been pick-axed through the brickwork the Citizen Army leader had to be transferred from his stretcher and carried in a sheet. In the course of his bearers' stumbling progress through the debris of the blacked-out little parlours, he suffered agonies; even *his* stubborn will betraying him into spasmodic, half-delirious cries of pain. During a brief halt his face was seen to be absolutely ashen, with glazed eyes staring from a mask of sweat. Plunkett too gave obvious cause for concern. In the last critical hours of the ordeals of the Post Office he had rallied magnificently, arousing himself from what many had thought his death-bed to help organise the fire-fighters and maintain morale. On the first lap of the journey he had astounded everyone by his energy. But such efforts had expended his last reserves of strength. He could not for long hold his old enemy at bay. Collapse must follow. Old Tom Clarke was also pretty well spent—the veteran Fenian was swaying on his feet.

Even should they succeed in their ambitious objective—to reach the barricade and clear the soldiers from it—it was obvious to Pearse that the rebels would not get far: not if the column was encumbered with the burdens of its wounded and its sick. Yet he could not—*would* not—leave his three comrades behind. To surrender them to the bullet or the rope was quite unthinkable. Besides there were also the wounded of the rank and file to consider, and also the three women. It was impossible to hasten the advance without causing intolerable hardship to these devoted people. It must—he declared—be sink or swim together.

It was with such factors as these in mind, then, that Padraic Pearse pressed on towards the Rising's inevitable ruin, and the military reprisals whose savagery would raise its spirit from the ashes. But before the column had inched even half of its way towards the barricade it appears to have become plain to him that the attempt had failed.

In the front parlour of 16 Moore Street he called a halt, and—together with Connolly—listened to the outline of an alternative plan. It was put forward by a boy of fifteen!

Willie MacLoughlin.

* * *

With the O'Rahilly dead, Connolly incapacitated, and the Boer War veteran MacBride isolated on the far side of the river, in Jacobs' factory, a scarcity of good leader-material was now making itself felt. However, Willy MacLoughlin was a General Staff in himself. His courage, cool-headedness, and complete self-confidence had for days past been remarked upon by the men at headquarters. Now—belatedly—they were beginning to recognise his wisdom. It was Willy who had warned his elders and betters of the strength of the British in the Moore Street area. It was Willy who had, presumptuously, advocated a fighting retreat to the Four Courts instead of one to the north. It was Willy who had tried—too late—to stop the O'Rahilly's charge. To Willy, Pearse and Connolly now turned with reviving hope.

The youngster had been promoted by Connolly in the field. As he spoke, he held the officer's sabre with which he had rallied his "command" a little earlier, during the first encounter with the British machine-guns. His new plan proposed that he and twenty volunteers took a route through the houses that would lead them to a spot only twenty yards short of the barricade. He would then launch a diversionary attack, to enable the main party to slip past the gap at the bottom of the road.

It was heroic stuff. It could be worth trying. But . . . Pearse asked "how many lives would we lose?"

"Twenty to thirty in Moore Street," the boy replied.

Deeply moved, the two leaders reluctantly gave their assent. By dawn, however, they had changed their minds again.

* * *

MacLoughlin, recalled when on the very verge of his attack, found Pearse consulting with Connolly. Both men looked worn and grim.

They had just witnessed at close quarters a typical example of what was happening to civilians caught up in the confusion of the battle.

A publican had fled from his burning house, accompanied by his wife and daughter. He was carrying a white flag as he led them, running towards the British barricade. The machine gunners had immediately opened fire. All three were dead.

The spectacle had been too much for Padraic Pearse. The retreat proposed by MacLoughlin would cause many similar tragedies, he said. More innocent civilians would lose their lives. He could not countenance it.

Then, to the gaping boy he added tersely: "You must order a cease-fire, to last for the next hour."

Pearse had made his final decision.

* * *

At 12.40 the men who manned the barricade at the top of Moore Street saw something move by the front door of number 16. Instinctively, they shot at it: then realised it was nothing more menacing than a stick. And tied to the stick was a white handkerchief. They ceased fire.

At 12.45 a nurse walked into the street. She was carrying a Red Cross flag. A brief silence fell, then the officer called to her to advance.

When she reached the barricade she paused, then recited with a sort of nervous firmness the bitter, heart-breaking words she had been ordered to say.

"The Commandant of the Irish Republican Army wishes to treat with the Commandant of the British Forces in Ireland."

Another brief silence, then the officer said: "The Irish Republican Army? The Sinn Feiners, you mean?"

Miss O'Farrell, for it was she, flushed angry red. "No. The Irish Republican Army they call themselves, and I think that is a very good name too . . ."

* * *

It was 2.30 in the afternoon when Padraic Pearse

approached the barricade, accompanied by Miss O'Farrell.

She had been sent back to him by General Lowe, with the news that surrender could only be unconditional. Unless Pearse gave up within the next half hour, the British would resume hostilities.

"Then let them," an officer had urged. "Let's fight to the bitter end!"

But Pearse had sadly shaken his head.

The time for fighting was over.

Escorted behind the barricade he came to a smart attention, and presented his sword to Lowe.

The latter, his back towards a tiny terrace-house and a full colonel on each side, took it with icy courtesy then brusquely came to the point. "My only concession is that I will allow the Commandants to surrender. Is that understood?"

Pearse nodded grimly.

Surrender orders were "forthwith" to be sent out to all local commands. And Miss O'Farrell would have the unpleasant job of delivering them.

For Pearse the car awaited that would first take him to the H.Q. of Irish Command, and thence to Arbour Hill Barracks —and to death.

*　　*　　*

"In order to prevent the further slaughter of Dublin citizens, and in the hope of saving the lives of our followers, now surrounded and hopelessly outnumbered, the members of the Provisional Government present at Headquarters have agreed to an unconditional surrender, and the Commandants of the various districts in the City and Country will order their commands to lay down arms . . ."

The instrument of surrender was signed by Pearse at 3.45 on Saturday the 29th of April.

It took a fair time to get to all the rebel outposts, and was greeted with near despair by the garrison of the Four Courts, where the local commander Holohan had to warn: "We came into this fight for Irish Independence in obedience to the commands of our higher officers and now in obedience with their wishes we must surrender."

At Bolands Mills, there was resentment too. To the huge crowd that had gathered to watch the rebels being marched into captivity, the gaunt de Valera snapped: "If only you had come out with your knives and forks and spoons."

At Jacobs' Factory, Kearney and his friends did not get the news until Sunday—or rather they refused to believe the news until it was personally confirmed to them by Hunter, who made his announcement in tears. As he gave the order, he broke his sword over his knee.

Carefully shaven, with beard neatly trimmed and his battle soiled uniform swapped for well-brushed tweeds, Boer War veteran Major MacBride lit a cheroot and then, shaking hands with each of his men with quiet finality, "There's a lesson in this for every one of you. If you get a chance of returning to the fight, never let yourselves be cooped up in a building again. Keep on the move."

It was a lesson that was to be taken to heart by the I.R.A. of the future, and, in one area was already being practised.

*   *   *

Not the least of the many ironies surrounding the conduct of the Easter fighting was the fact that, on the very day that was to end with the withdrawal of Pearse from the G.P.O. and be the immediate prelude to the surrender of the unsupported Dubliners, a Republican victory was being won in the open countryside that had hitherto remained so disappointingly quiet.

At Ashbourne, County Meath, the prototype of the I.R.A. "flying columns" of the future had engaged and defeated a force of fifty armed police. Thirty of them were casualties when the fight was over. The rebel losses were nil.

The Ashbourne ambush was a model that was to be imitated over and over again, in a different phase of Irish history: the savagery of the Troubles of the 'twenties.

But Pearse, on his way to captivity, was to know nothing of this. Not yet. When he did, he was to say at his court martial: "To refuse to fight would have been to lose; to fight is to win. We have kept faith with the past, and handed a tradition to the future . . ."

END OF A BEGINNING

The executions lasted for a week.

Pearse was the first to die, though not before writing a tender poem to his widowed mother, and comforting her by saying that soon all of them would see Papa again. Ironically, Papa had been an Englishman!

Connolly was the last to die. His wounds had not healed, so after he had kissed and embraced his family, he was carried in a chair to face the firing squad.

Plunkett was married in the death cell. He was shot four hours after putting the ring on his bride's finger.

MacBride went to death with a smile, and smoking a cheroot.

In all, fourteen of the rebel leaders were executed by Maxwell's stern decree. And one man who was not a leader, Willie Pearse. To this day it is said they shot him solely because he was Padraic's brother.

Trying to help the shattered city's morale, General Maxwell then paid a visit to the National Theatre. There he observed conversationally that the smoking ruins of Dublin reminded him of an oil painting he had once seen of The Last Days of Pompeii.

Somehow this honest soldier always said, and did, the wrong thing.

In the Royal Hospital the rebel flag was hung upside down on pikes.

Beyond those executed and imprisoned, some 3,000 suspects . . . Gaelic Leaguers . . . Sinn Feiners . . . Labourites . . . the lot who had failed to conform.

And Maxwell, as we know, became the bloody "Butcher."

Yet the General's actions, others argue, were not so very extreme. Not when considered against the passions of the hour, not when measured against the damage done.

The Rising had cost the Crown Forces over 600 casualties. The insurgents had lost maybe half that total, but it is difficult to say. The civilians suffered the most, with a tally of over 3,000 casualties, 450 of whom were dead.

The G.P.O., the Four Courts and Liberty Hall had been laid in ruins. So, too, had nine-tenths of O'Connell Street. Fifty percent of the city's stores had suffered severe damage.

From looting alone—blamed unfairly on the rebels—local traders were £3,000,000 the poorer. The total financial loss suffered by the city was said to have exceeded nearly ten times that sum.

No, looked at from the strictly legal angle, Maxwell was perfectly right.

Strategically, in the political sense, he was entirely wrong.

He had given Pearse precisely what he wanted. The rebel leader embraced death like a lover embracing his mistress.

The "sacrifice of blood" had been offered—and offered in full. Things in Ireland would never be the same again.

THE END

"General Maxwell, the British Commander-in-Chief, graced the National Theatre with his presence, and remarked to his entourage that the sight of Dublin in flames reminded him of the Last Days of Pompeii . . ."

> Peadar Kearney, reminiscing to his friends.

"It had an air of a Greek tragedy about it . . ."

> Michael Collins, in a letter from Frongoch internment camp.

"God Almighty, there was blood spilt enough that week . . . too much blood maybe, though we didn't think so at the time . . . blood between neighbours . . ."

> The author's cousin.

A SELECTION OF FINE READING
AVAILABLE IN CORGI BOOKS

Novels

☐ FN	7100	ANOTHER COUNTRY	James Baldwin	5/-
☐ GN	7335	THE SNOW BALL	Brigid Brophy	3/6
☐ GN	7284	SERENADE	James M. Cain	3/6
☐ GN	7319	THE BUTTERFLY	James M. Cain	3/6
☐ FN	7302	PRETTY LESLIE	R. V. Cassill	5/-
☐ FN	7317	THE CHINESE ROOM	Vivian Connell	5/-
☐ FN	7337	BEST SOUTH SEA STORIES		
			Edited by A. Grove Day and Carl Stroven	5/-
☐ FN	7283	THE CONFESSOR	Jackson Donahue	5/-
☐ FN	1278	THE GINGER MAN	J. P. Donleavy	5/-
☐ GN	7304	THE HOLLOW SHELL	John Farrimond	3/6
☐ GN	7072	DUST IN MY THROAT	John Farrimond	3/6
☐ FN	1500	CATCH-22	Joseph Heller	5/-
☐ FN	7354	GET HOME FREE	John Clellon Holmes	5/-
☐ EN	7193	MOTHERS AND DAUGHTERS	Evan Hunter	7/6
☐ GN	7236	A SHORT WALK TO THE STARS	Eric Lambert	3/6
☐ EN	7334	SPEAK NOT EVIL	Edwin Lanham	7/6
☐ GN	7320	THE UGLY AMERICAN	William J. Lederer and Eugene Burdick	3/6
☐ EN	7189	THE SAND PEBBLES	Richard McKenna	7/6
☐ XN	7335	AN END TO FURY	Edward Mannix	6/-
☐ FN	7301	WEEP NOT, MY WANTON	Nan Maynard	5/-
☐ XN	7351	CARAVANS	James A. Michener	6/-
☐ FN	7322	UNTAMED	Helga Moray	5/-
☐ FN	1066	LOLITA	Vladimir Nabokov	5/-
☐ FN	7203	APPOINTMENT IN SAMARRA	John O'Hara	5/-
☐ EN	7148	THE CAPE COD LIGHTER	John O'Hara	7/6
☐ XN	7251	ELIZABETH APPLETON	John O'Hara	6/-
☐ FN	7265	SERMONS AND SODA-WATER	John O'Hara	5/-
☐ XN	7266	ASSEMBLY	John O'Hara	6/-
☐ FN	1162	A STONE FOR DANNY FISHER	Harold Robbins	5/-
☐ FN	1187	79 PARK AVENUE	Harold Robbins	5/-
☐ FN	1204	NEVER LEAVE ME	Harold Robbins	2/6
☐ FN	7219	JUSTINE	The Marquis de Sade	7/6
☐ XN	7235	THE OSCAR	Richard Sale	6/-
☐ FN	1133	THE CARETAKERS	Dariel Telfer	5/-
☐ EN	7352	EXODUS	Leon Uris	7/6
☐ FN	7116	FOREVER AMBER Vol. I	Kathleen Winsor	5/-
☐ FN	7117	FOREVER AMBER Vol. II	Kathleen Winsor	5/-
☐ FN	7118	THE LOVERS	Kathleen Winsor	5/-
☐ FN	7222	STAR MONEY	Kathleen Winsor	5/-

All these great books are available at your local bookshop or newsagent; or can be ordered direct from the publisher. Just tick the titles you want and fill in the form below.

CORGI BOOKS, Cash Sales Department, Bashley Road, London, N.W.10.
Please send cheque or postal order. No currency, PLEASE. Allow 6d. per book to cover the cost of postage on orders of less than 6 books.

NAME ....

ADDRESS ....

(MAR. 66) ....